MW00615659

The Illustrated Mold Handbook

Ryglewicz • Vovk • Forde

W Marketing • Publisher
Hauppauge, NY

Copyright © 2003 W Marketing, Inc. All rights reserved.

Printed in the United States of America. Except as a protected under the United States of America Copyright Act of 1976, no part of this publication may be reproduced or distributed in any form or by any means, or stored in a data base or retrieval system, without the prior written consent of the publisher.

ISBN 0-9726296-1-0

For special quantity discounts on this and other technical titles, contact W Marketing at 30 Oser Avenue, Suite 500, Hauppauge NY, 11788 or call Construction Book Express at 800-253-0541.

The information contained in this book has been obtained by the publisher from sources believed to be reliable. W Marketing, the authors, printers or agents make no guarantee of the accuracy or completeness of any information published herein and neither W Marketing or its authors shall be responsible for any errors, omissions, or damages resulting out of the use of this information. It should be understood that W Marketing and the authors are offering information but are not attempting to render indoor air quality opinions, industrial hygiene evaluation, or any other microbial contamination service. If such services are required, the assistance of capable and qualified professionals should be sought.

CONTENTS

SECTION ONE

In The Beginning

IN THE BEGINNING THERE WAS MOLD AND IT'S STILL HERE.

Welcome to the Illustrated Mold Handbook

Firstly, is it mold or is it mould? The difference according to Dr. John Shane of McCrones Research Institute of Chicago is that mold is "*a container, and that mould is a fuzzy furry covered vessel.*" Therefore, it is possible to have mould in your mold. However, for this writing we use the word mold in the description of the spores, fungi, or contamination that we have encountered in hundreds of residential and commercial microbial investigations and indoor environmental reviews.

Mold is everywhere. It is not uncommon in the interior residential setting. How does it get inside? We carry it in, the dogs and cats carry it in, and it is driven by air with its ever-changing currents and eddies.

Mold has been around since biblical times, and according to scientists, even millions of years earlier. It can be found in artifacts of the past and even in outer space on the Mir Space Station.

Mold finds a home on cellulose products and cellulose containing items or other nutrients such as food, other molds, and even the human body. Mold is nature's disposal. Foods are contaminated with mold and are spoiled by the acids, compounds and toxins along with other metabolic products of fungi. Watch a white onion or an orange that is left in the refrigerator for endless weeks. (You will see nature at work; molds ahead: be careful; drive safely.)

Mold is a subset of Fungi, which is the Fifth Kingdom. A kingdom is a special group of organisms. They reproduce either asexually, which is anomorphic, or sexually which is telemorphic, and some times both, which is holomorphic.

In the following pages we will identify the causes of mold, how to find mold, how to sample mold, and how mold works in the indoor environment.

Water is one of the keys to successful mold amplification. In our microbial investigations, we are concerned with Water Activity, which is symbolized as AW. This is water available to the surface or substrate, which is one of the main conditions for fungal growth in buildings. Mold will find a suitable habitat in damp basements, on walls, ceilings, window frames, etc. Anything with a high AW has the ability to grow mold. The photographs in this book identify the sources of water infiltration in the home. Water activity is important. The water activity of a surface is the expression of the available moisture at equilibrium, and is defined as vapor pressure of water in the substrate, divided by the vapor pressure of pure water. This is .55 to 1.00. Molds are either hydrophylic (.85 to 1.00), mesophilic (around .75) or xerophylic (.65 to .55). These terms reflect much water, some water, and limited water, respectively.

One mold of particular interest is *Serpula lacrymans*, which is more commonly known as dry rot. This mold is famous for its destruction of building materials. The mold looks like a pile of rust with hyphae and rizoids that travel a long way. Moisture meters will not always identify this condition. You have to probe.

Most of the common molds in the house, or "household molds," are *Mytosporic fungi*. These include, but are not limited to, *Alternaria, Curvularia, Stachybotrys, Cladosporium, Fusarium,* and *Ulocladium.* The indoor air can also include *Rusts, Smuts,* and *Basidiomycetes.* There are simply thousands of fungi still unnamed.

Mold is everywhere. Its spores, or byproducts, may or may not bother you. Many people, after continual exposure to mold, can be sensitized. To those people that are immune-system compromised, mold is a clear and present danger. As inspectors, or homeowners, it is important to identify the conditions and eliminate the sources of water, nutrients, and ultimately, the mold itself.

SECTION TWO

Overview

INTRODUCTION

This book is a collection of site photographs and case studies of fungi contaminated locations. Included in this collection are selected articles and essays that can better inform both the layman and the investigator as to insights of the causes, sampling, health effects, locations and general information on the subject of fungi, the Fifth Kingdom.

If you compare your home or investigation site with the photographs in this book, you should hopefully be able to draw from the similarities between the actual and the photographed.

All of the photographs are of investigations that the authors have completed over the years of microbial investigations. There is information from other sources, whose names are listed in the acknowledgement section.

Included in this book are charts and graphs that we typically use on a daily basis to better understand the potential of microbial contamination and to practice "good science" with a standard of care and due diligence.

Only a person's individual health condition fosters the need to identify and to eliminate fungal growth for one's indoor environments. Our in-house laboratory analyzes tape lifts and Air-O-Cell cassettes. Below is a photomicrograph taken by Myron S. Ryglewicz, using a Cannon digital camera. Generally our reports and investigations include over eighty digital photographs of the conditions identified at the site. We firmly believe that a "picture is worth a thousand words."

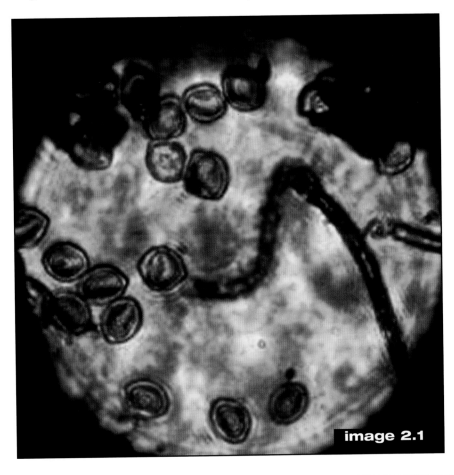

image 2.1

SECTION THREE

Fungus Basics

FUNGUS BASICS[1]

If you know nothing about the Fifth Kingdom or are practiced in microbial investigations, the following topics along with their specific concepts should become common knowledge to you. The basic areas of study should be spores, fungi, air, fungus, species, plants, mycelium, fruiting, fruiting bodies, nutrients, bacteria, toxins, vegetative stage, and growing. Also, some information on why fungus is hard to eliminate in structures is given.

Fungi have been placed in a kingdom by themselves. They are separate from plants, animals, and bacteria.

Fungi feed by sending out enzymes and absorbing soluble byproducts from their emmisions. They have cell walls composed of chitin, and reproduce by spores, in which each nucleus can germinate into a new individual.

Fungus spores in air can be distinguished from bacteria by size. Fungus spores can often be distinguished from pollen by their smaller size. Pollen grains are usually spherical, usually have unpigmented cell walls with internal sculpturing, and contain sporopollenin instead of chitin as cell wall composition. Fungi as a group are a very large and diverse assemblage of organisms. There are 69,000 species of fungi acknowledged in the latest edition of the *Dictionary of the Fungi*, 8th Ed. (Hawksworth 1995), with perhaps many more than that which have not yet been described in the scientific writings.

Fungi live in nearly every part of our environment, including the sea and lakes; most fungi have airborne spores and can theoretically end up in your air sample. This does not mean that you must be able to recognize 69,000 kinds of spores. A few readily recognizable spores are extremely common in air in every region of the earth and compose a major portion of air samples. All spores can be placed in a major category such as *Ascomycetes, Basidiomycetes, or Deuteromycetes.*

Many spores have never been identified because parts of it may have been missing, malformed, obscured or just too small to see under our microscopes.

It has been said that by standing at any single point on earth or in a room, sooner or later every kind of airborne spore will come to you. These will also come to your sampler.

Spores produced inside of buildings are important to identify so the investigator can determine their potential health effects, but the number of fungi capable of growing in buildings is limited. Most fungi gain their nutrients by breaking down (recycling) plant materials.

image 3.1

---

[1] J. Haines, et al. Mycology of the Air - a workshop manual for sampling and identifying airborne fungus spores.

image 3.2

scrub only until you remove the drywall or ceiling tile. The mold is still there, ready to grow back. The mycelium would be susceptible to disinfectants, but only if the disinfectant can reach it in the substrate. Mycelia is that which without moisture ceases to grow, becomes dormant, or dies. Without moisture it will have no effect on residence or its occupants.

All fungi are spore producing. Some spores are asexual and some are sexual that result from meiosis. Spores enter a very low metabolic state after they are formed, and are heavily protected from desiccation and toxins by a relatively impermeable chitin containing wall. The two primary functions of spores are to tide over unfavorable periods, and to disperse the fungus to new food sources (read as reproduction). Some can survive very high temperatures. Some can survive for hundreds of years. Spores can also survive large exposures to both man-made and naturally produced toxins. Spores are not easily killed by disinfectants. Imagine a fumigant that kills 99.9% of the *Aspergillus* spores from a colony covering a four-inch circle. Assuming 12,000,000 spores in the colony, the fumigation would leave 12,000 viable spores to start new colonies. A 99.9 percentage is not good enough in this case.

All fungi do not have predictable sporulating times. Some of the exceptions to this last statement are host specific *Ascomycetes,* and powdery mildews and mushrooms which have either Spring or Fall fruiting seasons. (Image 3.2)

Fungi have two distinct phases, vegetative and sporulating. The vegetative stage is composed of minute tubes called hyphae, and collectively called mycelia (think trees:forest). The mycelium is seen as the white fuzz laboratory cultures, but it is seldom seen in nature because the substrate it invades for nutrients, is usually opaque. The mycelium is the site of growth, nutritional uptake, and, in some species, toxin production. The function of the mycelium is to take in nutrients from its surroundings and proliferate through the food source. The mycelium is very susceptible to desiccation, the starvation from lack of nutrients and toxins.

Some species grow very quickly, utilize easily available sugars, and die out in a matter of days or weeks. Other fungi may persist and grow literally for hundreds of years.

Most of the fungi we deal with are in homes and, as allergens, have a short life span. The vegetative stage is deep in its food source, i.e., drywall or ceiling tile for example; it literally can't be scrubbed off. Don't waste your elbow grease. Brush and

image 3.3

image 3.4

image 3.5

The good news here is that without moisture, the spores are just dust and cannot pose an immediate threat to a building. The bad news is that the allergic components of fungi are proteins, and other large molecules, on the outside of the spore wall.

Spores may be allergenic whether they are dead or alive. Be advised that if you use a toxin to kill the spore, you then have created a toxic, allergenic spore. Most dead spores on building surfaces can be removed by extreme elbow grease and washing.

Most fungi form one or more structures called fruiting bodies on the mycelium, and it is on this structure that the spores are formed. The sole purpose of the fruiting body is to help protect and disperse the spores. Examples of fruiting bodies are mushrooms, bracket or shelf fungi as found on trees, and the innumerable, minute, black spheres filled with spores on leaves and twigs. When the mycelium runs out of water or nutrient, encounters cold temperatures which signal the end of the growing season, or encounters a buildup of toxins from a competing species, it stops growing and literally channels its cytoplasm into the formation of a fruiting body and spore producing cells. No one should be surprised that millions of *Basidiomycete* spores invade the air after a rain and that they are nearly absent on a dry day.

The classification and naming of fungi is very complex. This is due to the logical desire to make the system of names follow natural relationships and to be governed by standard rules. There are many books and web sites that categorically list the techniques of fungi classification. By seeing the number of times that a species has been cited, an indication is given as to which species are most common. By charting, graphing, and collecting information along with good record keeping, then and only then can you draw conclusions on what genus is significant to your area.

Mold is usually a function of a water infiltration, humidity, and an elevated water activity AW level.

Notice in Image 3.6 how the mold mycelium was amplifying on the rafters and interior wall cavities. This condition was identified only after the drywall was removed. The drywall had sags and mold growing on the surface. The leak was on the second level over thirty feet from this location.

image 3.6

SAMPLE BASICS[1]

Types of Samples

Moisture measurements are recorded to establish a pattern of excess moisture in building materials and to determine if there is excess moisture, temperature, and humidity. Excess humidity in the indoor environment can lead to amplification of molds on building materials, clothing, shoes and other furnishings.

Relative humidity on a surface of 50% to 70% and above will sustain the growth of some species of fungi. Moisture load refers to how much moisture is in the air and is temperature dependent. This is reported as grains of moisture.

Microbial refers to fungi or bacteria. Mold and mildew are common names for fungi.

Tape lifts are used on visible fungal growth to determine if it is fungal growth and what genus it is. This type of sample cannot determine the extent of the growth, only the identification. We also use this type of sample on dusty hard surfaces to look for indications of growing fungi nearby, as determined by large chains of clumps of spores.

Surface samples can be collected on growth media. A Rodac plate is pressed to the surface to be evaluated and incubated at room temperature. Also, any resulting colonies should be identified. A Rodac plate is a small plastic Petri dish filled with growth media that has a convex or curved surface, so it can be rolled over the surface to be evaluated (Image 4.1).

Results can be reported in various ways. In general, if the sample were collected from a surface with no obvious fungal growth and there is a variety of fungal types identified and 25 or less CFU per Rodac surface, the surface is normal. If there are a number of the same colony types such as *Penicillium* or *Aspergillus*, even if less than 25 CFU, it can be an indication of excess moisture at the surface evaluated allowing fungal amplification. (A plate covered with fungal colonies is an indication of fungal contamination on the surface being evaluated, or a heavier than normal fall out of fungal spores.)

Sterile swabs can also be used to collect samples from surfaces. These can be evaluated directly; the swab can be inoculated on the media or can be placed into a diluent and treated as a bulk sample.

Bulk samples can also be collected (Image 4.2). These can be dust collected by vacuuming, pieces of drywall, carpet, wall paper, cloth, or other porous material you suspect of having fungal growth. Usually a small portion of the material one-gram or less is weighed, placed into a diluent, mixed thoroughly, and then serially diluted onto appropriate growth media. The results are then reported as CFU/gram.

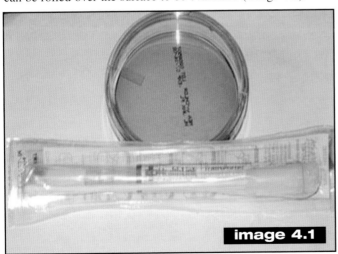

image 4.1

image 4.2

Spore Trap samples are collected to determine what particles are in the air. If the spore load is high in a spore trap sample, it can be an indication that there is fungal growth near by. Results are reported as counts per cubic meter of air (C/m3). When clumps of spores are present, every spore is counted.

Some spores are viable - that is, they are alive and able to grow into a colony of whatever type of fungi they are. Some spores are non-viable or "not alive". A spore can be allergenic, irritating, sensitizing and/or toxigenic whether it is viable or non-viable. A dead spore is just as much of a problem as a live spore.

The most common instruments used to collect spore trap samples are the Allergenco, Burkart and the Air -0- Cell cassette. Each of these samplers has a small slit in the top and a pump which sucks air in through the slit causing particles in the air to adhere (impact) to a sticky surface on a microscope slide inside the instrument. The area where the particles stick is called a track or trace. The trace is stained, covered with a cover slip, and evaluated by using a microscope.

Analysis of spore traps requires counting the trace under 400, 600 and 1,000 power with a bright field microscope. Not everything seen on a spore trap is a spore. Other particles can also be present in spore trap samples. Pollen, insect parts, combustion particles, tire particles, fiberglass, diatomaceous earth, and other particle types can be identified. Higher than normally seen, levels of any particle type can be a cause for further investigation

Interpreting spore trap results requires comparing outdoor reference samples with samples from the complaint indoor location. When the percentage of *Aspergillus/Penicillium* spores exceeds that of *Cladosporium* and there are 1,000C/m3 or more of *Asp/Pen* spores it is a good indication of amplification. If there is a spore type that is known to be able to amplify indoors that is present in significant numbers and not present in outdoor samples, a source of that spore may be present. (Examples would be *Chaetomium, Alternaria,* and *Stachybotrys.*)

Elevated levels of *Cladosporium* can also be an indication of amplification of that fungal genus indoors, if levels outdoors are low.

Culturable samples reflect which fungi are able to grow under laboratory conditions on artificial media. Not all types of fungi will grow on standard media used for environmental evaluation. Growing the fungi enables the lab to identify the fungi to genera and often, to species. Example, *Stachybotrys chartarum; Stachybotrys* is the genus or genera, and *chartarum* is the species.

Air samples are usually collected with the Andersen. The Andersen N6 sampler is a three-part machined aluminum device designed to impact spore size particles onto a growth medium surface. (1) There is a cover which contains a hole through which air is sucked, (2) a plate which has 400 holes through which the air must pass and (3) a bottom plate which holds a Petri dish with appropriate growth medium where any spores that are sucked through the 400 holes will impact. A pump is hooked to the sampler to draw the air into the sampler. The pump is calibrated to draw in 28.3 liters per minute. A mathematical formula is used to convert the results to CFU/m3.

The Petri dishes that have been exposed to the air in the Andersen sampler are incubated at room temperature (25°C) for 5 - 7 days to allow any culturable fungi that may have been in the air-stream to grow. Once the fungi grow, they are visible on the surface of the growth media in the Petri dish and can be counted and identified. The results are reported as colony forming units per cubic meter of air (CFU/m3). More than one spore may be responsible for a single colony-forming unit. (In spore traps every spore is counted; therefore, spore levels are usually higher than culturable colony forming units.)

Interpreting culturable fungal levels requires comparing outdoors and non-complaint areas with the complaint area or areas. The distribution of fungal types should be similar. If the laboratory you use does not calculate rank order or percentages, this is something you will have to do.

image 4.3

A clean area, where we are searching for unknowns.

image 4.4

A very contaminated area, where we are searching for how much.

[1] *So What Does It Mean?* Prepared by Connie Jenkins for Environmental Testing & Technology

SECTION FIVE

More On Sampling

SAMPLING SPECIFICS

The Air-O-Cell™ Air sampling cassette is a sampling device designed for the rapid collection and analysis of a wide range of airborne aerosols. Air enters the cassette, the particles become impacted on the sampling substrate, and the air leaves through the exit nipple. The airflow and patented cassette housing is designed in such a way that the particles are distributed and deposited equally on a special glass slide contained in the cassette housing called the "trace." This method is useful for initial site testing, especially if fungal growth is not visible.

Fungi cannot be fully speciated with this method. *Aspergillus* and *Penicillium* are normally reported together due to the similarities in spore morphology. The cassette is designed to operate at a recommended flow rate of 15 lpm. Lower flow rates may result in a loss of some spores and the accumulation of others in a non-uniform manner. Higher flow rates may damage the spores, reducing the prospect of accurate identification.

A specially designed bubble tube, available from the manufacturer, called a rotameter, can be used to set the flow rate for the Air-O-Cell™ mini pump. The sampling time is dependent on the density of particulate in the environment. It is important not to overload the sample; otherwise it will be impossible to assess the types of spores, pollen, and particulate that are present. Prior to sampling, calibrate the pump to 15 liters per minute. Remove and retain tape seal covering Air-O-Cell™ inlet and outlet. Attach the outlet (round hole) to the supplied tubing adapter (available upon request), or use standard PVC tubing (for use with high volume pumps only). Start the sampling pump, and sample for an appropriate period of time. Remove Air-O-Cell™ from tubing, and reseal with the original tape.

It is important to document your sample by completing a Chain of Custody (CoC), which contains the client name and information, project name or number, sample number or identification, description of area, and volume of air used. An effective interpretation is based on the comparison of indoor and outdoor samples. An outdoor sample will help demonstrate whether spore amplification is occurring indoors. Obtain a control sample from a non-complaint area for comparison. Sending a blank cassette for analysis periodically is a good practice. Flow rate is critical for accurate results. Remember to calibrate and recalibrate the pump prior to all sampling. Never use cassettes that are damaged or expired.

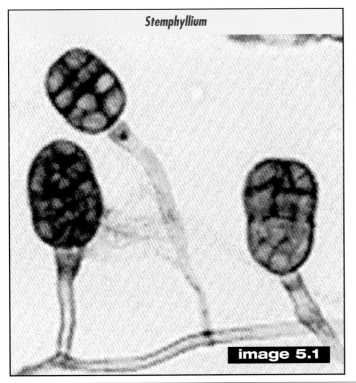

Stemphyllium

image 5.1

You, and you alone decide what tests to take and where to take them. This knowledge only comes through education and practice.

Anderson Impact sampling

This method of air sampling involves drawing a measured volume of air over culture media in Petri dishes.

The Petri dishes[1] are incubated in the laboratory so the organisms impacted on the plate can grow. The fungi or bacteria are counted and identified. This method commonly uses the Andersen N-6 Impactor ™. Different media are available from the laboratories, depending on whether fungi or bacteria are to be identified. Fungal cultures can determine whether spores are viable (alive), and allow for more specific identification. Bacterial cultures provide enumeration and identification of viable bacteria present in the air. Cultures take six to ten days for the bacterial cells or fungal spores to grow and be identified.

Even though non-viable spores will not grow using this method, they can be significant, causing allergic reactions or irritation to some people.

Since most environmental specimens contain a large number of organisms, each has to compete with others to grow on the media. As a result, fungi and bacteria present in the air may not be as well represented in culture. Some fungi do not grow well or at all in culture. Some organisms are unable to be identified, as they fail to produce spores, or have not yet been scientifically characterized. Agar plates must be kept refrigerated or on ice until ready to use. These plates need to be at room temperature in order for the spores to be properly impacted in the agar. Do not remove the lid from the plate at any time, except during sampling.

The plates must be shipped on ice with OVERNIGHT PRIORITY.

Use adequate packing material to protect the plates. The weight of the icepack can crush the plates during shipping. Plates must not come into direct contact with the ice, as the tests will be invalid if the media freezes. A Chain of Custody must accompany the plates. Note on the CoC, the date collected and the date that the sample was sent to the laboratory.

Tape Lifts

Take a few inches of clear tape. Avoid touching the sticky side, especially the part touching the mold. Be sure to be wearing gloves, apply the central inch of tape to the suspect area (choose one that is free of extraneous debris). Apply light pressure to the non-adhesive side. Pull tape off surface with slow, steady pressure, holding the tape edges only. Apply the sticky side of tape to the inside of the plastic bag. Ensure there are no folds or creases in the tape. Put only one sample in each bag. Label and identify each sample.

Swab Samples

Wearing gloves, remove swab from packaging material. Swab the desired area thoroughly, rolling the swab lightly back and forth over sampling area. Insert the swab in the tube, and firmly close cap. Complete a Chain of Custody (CoC), detailing client name and information, project name or number, sample number, and a description of the area.

image 5.2

Air-O-Cell™ sampling is done on the exterior to establish a baseline. This is very important to your sampling strategy. This test is a non-viable test. Anderson impact samples give a viable sample. Particle counting, odor testing, carbon dioxide and carbon monoxide are all sampled at the time of the air sampling.

image 5.3

---

[1] The Sampling Supplies Request form is available from the EMSL Analytical, Inc. website (www.emsl.com)

SECTION SIX

How Moisture Infiltrates Dwellings

WAYS MOISTURE INFILTRATES DWELLINGS

Moisture can cause serious damage to the structure of your home. Moisture causes more than $1 billion in damage to homes annually, from minor damage like peeling paint, to major damage, such as rotting, crumbling structural floor joists.

You can greatly reduce the cost of moisture damage in your home and eliminate the risk of structural loss if you learn how to control moisture. It is important to control all sources of moisture that enters a home. Most moisture that is generally known to cause problems in homes is roof leaks, basement leaks, and plumbing leaks. These three types of leaks are the most obvious.

Roof Leaks

In the average year, three feet of water hits a house—that is 75 tons or roughly 518,400 raindrops by a mathmatical estimate. The question frequently asked by resale home buyers (after asking about basement leaks) is, "Does the roof leak?" Roofs are exposed to tremendous environmental stresses - rain, snow, ice, sun, and extreme temperatures. Eventually, the materials wear out and require replacement to keep your house dry. A typical shingle roof will require replacement after 16 years. There are other factors that greatly effect the useful life of a roof such as, quantity and quality of ventilation, number of roofing layers, foliage overhang, installation quality, etc.

Many roofs are hazardous and dangerous to walk on. Your inspection will only be based on what is visible from the ground level with or without binoculars. Only professional roofers should walk on rooftops. Shingles are soft in hot weather, and brittle in cold weather. Minimize walking on the roof during temperature extremes. Do not chip ice from a roof - you will do more damage than good. I have heard that you can use a low-pressure washer with warm water to remove ice dams. Roofs and ladders can also be very slippery. Your safest call would be to a roofing professional who has the knowledge and safety equipment to assess and correct your roof leakage problems, if they exist.

The condition of a flat, metal, or built-up roof often cannot be determined unless it is possible to closely inspect its surface. All slate, tile, and concrete roofs will require yearly inspection and possibly yearly repairs. Older slate, tile, and concrete roofs, become more sensitive to weather and tend to crack, chip, or become loose, and require more maintenance then other roof types. Life expectancy of new roofs in years.:

Asphalt /Fiberglass	16-25 years
Wood	16-40 years
Slate	60-100 years
Roll	7-10 years
Tile	40-60 years
Metal	20-60 years
Asbestos	35-50 years

Most common causes of roof leaks:

- Improper flashing, sealing or worn through flashing around projections through the roof such as, plumbing stacks (vent pipes), chimneys, skylights, antennas, dormers, etc.
- Missing, broken or pierced shingles caused by stones, hail, broken branches or walking on a roof
- Tears or deterioration in valleys, caused by expansion and contraction or someone walking in the valley. In addition, debris can build up in a valley and block its run-off process causing rain and snow to build up and cause excessive damage.
- Exposed nails, nails in the wrong places, or nails not set flush with the underlying shingles
- Wind driven rain may enter through the chimney, brick, mortar or under shingles. In addition, through the siding and behind the step flashing, where a lower roof joins the vertical side of the main house.
- Ice dams, which prevent water run-off, force standing water behind the ice dam, to backup under your roof shingles.
- Improperly hung gutters or drip edge
- Improperly installed roofing, or a roofing type, which is incorrect for the slope of the roof involved
- Cracking and blistering of roof mastic on rolled asphalt or on built up roofing
- Ponds of water, created when flat or low-sloped roofs begin to sag
- Clogged roof and gutter drains

It is possible to have more that one type of roofing when you have multiple membranes. When downspouts and gutters are not properly maintained on garages and dwellings, poor drainage can cause seepage into the dwelling. All gutters and downspouts should be free of debris and properly installed.

Many times, past property owners disconnect downspouts at the base and install splash type blocks. These types of repairs might be indicators of past seepage, which the present owner should disclose. Penetrations at vents and chimneys and roof flashing should be inspected periodically for deterioration and possible leaks.

Basement Leaks

A damp and musty basement is not only unpleasant; it can also adversely affect the health of the occupants. Most basement moisture problems can be easily recognized by doing a thorough and systematic inspection of the basement, looking for any problems in corners, between basement walls and floor slab, behind furniture, underneath carpet, ceilings, at outside sheathing, and around windows.

Most common causes of basement leaks:
- Water penetrating through foundation walls
- Water penetrating through foundation floor
- Standing water on floor
- Water stains on concrete blocks
- Damp, humid air
- Condensation or dew points on cold walls, band joists and floor in heating seasons
- Condensation on vapor retarders in cooling seasons
- Odor, mold and mildew
- Buckling of wood and lifting-up of floor tiles and carpeting
- Staining or rot of wood headers, joists, framing and sill plates
- Staining and blistering of wall covering

Special note to prospective new homebuyers

Basement leaks occur from many different types of conditions. Prior to purchasing a home, is important for prospective buyers to perform several steps. Prospective buyers should have a professional inspector or engineer look the foundation walls. When walls are recently painted and patched, foundation conditions are often difficult to determine. The prospective buyers need to ask previous homeowners what the walls looked like prior to the painting and patching. The prospective buyer should also investigate and inquire if there were ever sewer backups, tree root blockage, foundation conditions, flooding, structural conditions, soil movements, or any other notable condition that ever existed or occurred prior to purchasing this home. This can be done by checking city records for permits, asking adjacent neighbors questions about past conditions, searching old real-estate records for past sales, reading past home inspection reports, or any other resource that would provide more knowledge. Basement moisture or seepage is frequently mentioned on property disclosure forms. It is not the duty of the inspector or engineer to interpret these comments. Clients should personally ask sellers if past seepage, moisture, mold, flooding, run-off problems, erosion, sewer back-up, sewer odor, musty odor, underground conditions, structural repairs, settlement, cracks, water-proofing, or any other moisture or structural related conditions ever existed with the foundation or dwelling in the past. All basement and crawl defects such as cracks, leaks, settlement, mold, mildew, unlevel conditions, and other uncommon conditions, require second opinions. The prospective buyer should also get a warranty on any waterproofing or structural repair that has been done in the past. When basement walls are covered by paneling or drywall, potential moisture, or mold conditions may exist behind walls. Dismantling the finished systems for observation is usually necessary for a proper examination.

Plumbing Leaks

Plumbing leaks occur from many different sources. In older homes, they occur from corrosion of galvanized pipes or rusting sanitary lines. In newer homes, plumbing leaks occur from defective plastic pipes or failed plumbing systems. In homes with surrounding trees, plumbing leaks occur from tree root back up. In all homes, plumbing leaks occur from poor maintenance of fixtures, leaking wax seals, loose drains under sinks, dripping faucets, leaking supply lines, cracked stacks and more. The most common major plumbing leaks are frozen pipes and overflows. When claiming insurance, the term overflow should be used. Terms such as back up, blockage and clogged drains may not be covered by insurance carriers. Long-term plumbing leaks will cause microbial fungal reservoirs.

Moisture movement is much more complex than just the three above-mentioned methods. Below we have listed seven methods where moisture can enter a home.

Moisture can enter the home through the following methods:
1. Rainwater
2. Groundwater
3. Capillary suction below grade
4. Capillary suction above grade
5. Air movements
6. Air pressure
7. Vapor diffusion

WATER ENTRY METHODS

Rainwater

Rainwater is the most common water penetration culprit. Rainwater can leak into buildings from roofs, overhangs, building envelopes and foundations. It is imperative that rainwater be shed or controlled away from the building components. Strategic building placement can minimize wind driven rain leaks. Proper building roof overhangs will shed water away, and architectural detailing of construction materials installation will minimize moisture migration into building systems. These are the obvious and conventional rainwater control methods. Others may be necessary based on grade, soil percolation, or vegetation conditions.

Less obvious means of rainwater entry are air pressure difference, momentum, surface tension, and gravity. If the exterior pressure is higher than that of the pressure in the wall cavity, the rainwater can be drawn into the wall cavity. It is important to have equal pressure on the exterior and interior of the wall. If straight horizontal wall penetrations exist, rainwater can be drawn into the wall cavity through momentum. By installing key-ways or upward angles in wall systems, rainwater momentum can be diminished. If kerfs or drip edges do not exist in wall penetrations, rainwater can enter through surface tension. If flashing is missing, rainwater can be drawn into the wall cavity through gravity. These are all conditions that should be evaluated prior to construction. Two installations that control these types of entry are rain screens and flashings.

A typical rain screen and flashing example is properly installed brick siding. The gap or air space that is 3/8-1/2 inch in size behind the brick serves as a rain screen to allow water to flow downward. The weep holes at the bottom cause pressure equalization within the wall cavity and allow water to exit. The flashing at the base or at weep whole area stops water from migrating into the building envelopes. This brick system also should also have a vapor barrier or damp-proofing membrane on the exterior side of the sheathing, or masonry, or other construction material that is exposed in this small space or gap. When systems are properly installed, all four moisture intrusion mechanisms, air pressure difference, momentum, surface tension, and gravity are controlled.

Vinyl and aluminum siding are rain screens because they both have air gaps on the backside for water to drain, and weep holes for water to exit.

Groundwater

Groundwater is the second leading cause of moisture in dwellings. The most effective groundwater strategy to minimize moisture infiltration is proper foundation grading. A declining slope of one inch per foot for the first five feet is optimal. This declining slope allows water to run away from the foundation. The soil at this area should be clay or impermeable so water cannot easily be absorbed.

Proper foundation drainage systems are needed to ensure that moisture migration into the building systems does not occur. The foundation backfill should be porous and allow gravity to pull the water down the drain tile system. The foundation walls should be properly damp-proofed so water is not absorbed into the foundation wall system. The drain tiles should be installed to allow water to travel away from the structure.

Many older foundation wall systems crack, bow, or fail. They fail from initial under-designed foundation wall systems, from hydrostatic loading of wet soil, footing settlement, soil loading, or other conditions. In many older homes, drain-tile systems fail and the exterior soil becomes heavy and water saturated. This heavier soil exerts more pressure to the wall and causes cracks. Cracks penetrate through the entire foundation wall and a leak results. Many homes that have finished basement walls with leaking cracks have interstitial mold reservoirs. Everytime it rains, the cracks leak water, and mold behind the walls amplifies. These cracks can also leak from poor grade, sprinkler heads being too close to the foundation, leaking gutters, or leaking or spilling downspouts.

Vertical cracks generally are shrinkage type cracks. Vertical cracks do have the potential to leak and get larger over time. When this condition occurs, digging the exterior and waterproofing the crack is necessary. Horizontal cracks, step cracks, and combinations are signs of soil movement and soil pressure. These horizontal and step crack conditions can be caused by, and not limited to wet heavy clay, under-designed foundations, poor drainage, poor grading, excessive soil on the exterior foundation wall or other exterior loading conditions. Horizontal and step crack conditions often get worse over time and often require structural maintenance or repairs. Horizontal and step cracks can get larger, leak water, and cause upper structural distress. We recommend that you get a second opinion from a structural engineer to determine soundness and integrity of all horizontal and step crack conditions. These can indicate substantial and expensive structural problems and should be evaluated by a professional.

Capillary Action Below Grade

Capillary action below grade is the absorption of moisture in porous materials. This is why damp proofing or waterproofing of foundations is necessary. The porous foundation material must be sealed so moisture cannot be absorbed. An example of capillary action can be seen sometimes in garages. The garage foundation block will have efflorescence stains (white, irregular, powdery residue) in the interior of the garage foundation masonry block. This condition occurs because builders generally will not waterproof or damp-proof garage foundations. All brick or foundation material that is to be buried in soil or exposed to soil should be sealed, waterproofed, or damp-proofed. Many slab homes have conditions caused by capillary action below grade. Many older slabs in homes were poured with no vapor barrier and no coarse aggregate substrate. Moisture can be absorbed into the slab material when these types of conditions exist. Many times, you will see moisture stains or efflorescence stains in cracks. Other times you will see heaving of slabs. Heaving of slabs is also hydrostatic pressure related. It is important to install stone below the slab and a vapor barrier just under the slab to control capillary action. Sometimes this condition is also referred to as damp-rise.

Capillary Action Above Grade

Capillary action above grade is the absorption of moisture in porous materials. The most common is wood siding. Wood siding is porous and absorbent. This is why we seal and paint wood siding. The sealant or paint membrane seal off the porous wood, making the system less absorbent. When installing cedar shakes or shingles it is advised to also install firring strips being the wood siding. This is to allow the wood to dry out if it becomes wet.

Brick siding is a good example of capillary action above grade. When brick becomes wet, during rainfall, it will absorb moisture. If wet brick is exposed to sunlight, then moisture will travel further into the brick through capillary action and vapor

diffusion. As mentioned earlier, these brick systems need drain screens to move the unwanted moisture away from the inner building components.

Another example of control of capillary action is wood shingle and shake roofs. The wood will absorb moisture through capillary action. The wood roof shingles or shakes need firring strips. The firring strips will allow the moisture to dry out on both sides. Also building paper is needed to be installed over the firring strips to serve as a moisture barrier.

Air Movement

Air can move into the building from the exterior. Air can move out of the building from the interior. Air is not a moisture problem unless it is also carrying moisture or humidity. Air that carries moisture through the building envelope, can deposit some of this moisture within the building envelope through dew points or condensation. We cannot control the exterior moisture in the air due to nature, but we can control the interior air that contains moisture. Interior moisture levels can be controlled several ways. The three main ways to control moisture are to control the source of moisture, mixing the moist air with non-moist air, and using a dehumidifier.

Controlling the source of the moisture is very important. If moisture is not initially put into the air, than we do not have to remove it. Moisture that enters a home from foundation walls of dirt crawl space floors, are a major source of water entry into building systems today. When building new, you must properly install foundation drainage and you must properly install vapor barriers. Other sources of moisture that are indoors are as follows:

Moisture source in home	Estd. moisture in pints
Bathing tub (excludes towel and spillage)	0.12 standard size bath
Bathing shower (excludes towel and spillage)	0.53/5-minute shower
Clothes washing (automatic, lid closed)	0
Clothes drying (vented outdoors)	0
Clothes drying (vented indoors)	4.68 to 6.16 load electric
Clothes drying (vented indoors)	4.68+ to 6.16+ load gas
Combustion (un-vented kerosene space heater)	7.6/gallon of kerosene
Combustion back drafting or spillage	0 to 6,720+/year
Cooking breakfast for family of four	0.35 (plus 0.58 if gas)
Cooking lunch for family of four	0.53 (plus 0.68 if gas)
Cooking dinner for family of four	1.22 (plus 1.58 if gas)
Cooking simmer at 203°F/10 min/6 inch pan	0.13

Moisture source in home	Estd. moisture in pints
Cooking boil 10 minutes 6 inch pan	0.48 (0.57 uncovered)
Desorption of material seasonal	6.33 to 16.91 average day
Desorption of material new construction	10+ average day
Dishwashing breakfast	0.21
Dishwashing lunch	0.16
Dishwashing dinner	0.68
Firewood storage indoors (cord of green wood)	600/6months
Floor mopping	.03/square foot
Gas range pilot light (each)	0.37/day
House plants 5-7 total	0.86 to 0.96day
Humidifiers	120+ /day or2.08 ave./hr
Pet's	fraction
Respiration perspiration family of four	0.44/hour
Refrigerator defrost	1.03/day
Saunas, steam baths, and whirlpools	0 to 2.7+ / hour

It is actually amazing how much moisture a home could produce.

Example:
- Family of four on a football Sunday in a winter month
- New 2000 Sq/ft tight home with house wrap
- New high efficient furnace with humidifier that is on
- Ventless fireplace that is on all night
- Seven nice plants in home throughout
- All home cooked meals
- Washed 1000 Sq/ft of floors during cleaning
- Treadmill used by two occupants for 30 minutes each

This home could produce up to 15 gallons of water that will contribute to the humidity in the home.

Mixing the moist air with non-moist air, helps in minimizing dew points or condensation. This method will not generally work in warmer climates due to the mixing air, which generally is the exterior air, that contains higher moisture content or humidity than that of the interior air. In the winter months, using cold exterior low-humidity air for mixing may not be thermally efficient.

Dehumidification is the most common moisture control. Many homes with leaking foundations cannot afford new waterproofing systems, so the homeowners plug in dehumidifiers. In summer months, air dehumidification occurs during the use of air conditioning. Moisture is removed from the drain pan as water drips from the evaporator. It is important to evaluate the disposal of this condensate so it is not removed from the air, only to be re-evaporated into the interior environment.

Air Pressure

Pressure in homes is an important element in determining a healthy or un-healthy environment. If your home is sucking air, it is depressurized (has a negative pressure). If you were to close all the windows, seal all the exterior wall penetrations, and then turn on an attic fan, house fan, clothes dryer, or a bathroom fan, the home would be sucking air and possibly become depressurized. These mechanical units are moving air from the inside of the home to the outside of the home. If you removed house air, new air must replace the space. This air can come from wall cracks, crawl spaces, chimneys or stacks, interstitial walls, leaking doors, leaking windows, stucco cracks, weep holes, wall penetrations, construction holes, and other venting areas.

Dwellings and buildings all leak air. Interior or conditioned air escapes, and outside air is sucked in. This outside air is not conditioned and contains moisture and potential mold spores. These conditions can seriously add to the problem of indoor air quality, sick building syndrome, building related illness, smoke and fire spread, condensation, radon, corrosion, decay, deterioration, humidity, odor, energy consumption, maintenance, and added housekeeping.

The following are the three natural conditions that can change the pressure in your home:

Wind Effect

When the wind blows against the dwelling, it creates a high-pressure area on the windward side and air is forced into the dwelling. A low-pressure area is created on the leeward side where air is drawn out of the home. This causes depressurization and possible moist air infiltration.

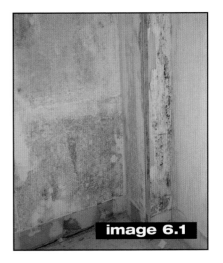
image 6.1

Many homes near oceans and lakes have moisture or odor problems. The large water mass has no obstructions and the wind directly hits the ocean side. A musty crawl space would be depressurized and all the crawl air could end up in the upper dwelling. If the bathroom faces the waterside, look behind the vinyl wallpaper for mold.

A more common example is a high-rise hotel near the water. Many of these buildings are mold-infested and wind effect is definitely a contributor.

image 6.2

Image 6.1 was taken on the east side of a hotel located facing the Atlantic Ocean. The vinyl wallpaper was removed and mold was exposed. The remodeling company was not wearing PPE and no mold abatement strategies were implemented.

Image 6.2, was the fifth story outside wall, facing Lake Erie. On this particular wall, you could actually see the mold reservoirs through the wallpaper. Many times, you will see pink or gray blemishes. These were gray. We are not solely blaming wind effect in either of these two examples because other factors were also contributors.

Stack Effect

In a conditioned or heated building, less dense warm air rises, then expands, creating a higher-pressure area near the upper elevation. This air escapes through holes or penetrations in the ceiling. This air also escapes through leaking windows, doors, and other mechanical penetrations. The force of the ris-

image 6.3

ing air creates lower pressure near the bottom of the building. This is also known as negative pressure or depressurization. This condition causes outside or soil air to rush in through cracks and openings in the lower levels of the structure. Stack effect may have some correla-

tion with odor concentrations. As stack pressure increases, so do odor levels. The two main variables that affect the stack effect, are temperature and building elevation. The colder the exterior temperature, the greater the stack effect. The higher the building elevation, the greater the stack effect.

Combustion and Ventilation Effects

Appliances that burn fossil fuels or manufactured fuels need air to support combustion and provide the draft in the

image 6.4

chimney. This negative pressure air is replaced by outside air through unintentional openings in the building envelope. This is why people often notice that a room becomes drafty when there is a fire in the fire-place.[2] The room is now depressurized. That means this room may be sucking air from other undesirable areas, primarily unconditioned exterior air.

In newer homes, many furnaces or hot water heaters have power vented exhaust systems. These white PVC pipes stick out of siding on residential dwellings. These pipes are taking air out of the home. For every action, there is an equal and opposite reaction; air must come from somewhere to replace this exhausted air. This can depressurize a basement and cause moisture to be sucked through cracks in basement walls. This moisture can cause upper levels of humidity and dew points. Achieved dew points usually equal mold.

image 6.5

We will get calls on certain winter days in northeastern Ohio. The call comes in and the prospective client says, "Water is dripping behind all my basement insulation." When we arrive, we will see sections of insulation fastened to the basement walls. The insulation is foil-faced with the foil side exposed. The basement is tight and insulated, and the door to the area is closed. The newer high efficient furnace has a power driven exhaust, installed with no make up air wall penetrations. The basement lacks a dehumidifier. The furnace is sucking out the basement moisture. This basement is depressurized and mois-ture is being sucked out of the soil through foundation walls and shrinkage cracks. This moisture dissipates and creates high humidity that is trapped behind the insulation. The ground is cold and the humidity reaches dew point behind the insulation. This is why the insulation is dripping moisture to the floor. The process is as follows: depressurization causes moisture infiltra-tion, then high humidity, resulting in dew point, which ulti-mately causes mold reservoirs. All you need to do is remove one of the variables, and this phenomenon is ceased.

Some other ventilation effects that created dwelling depressurization were clothes dryers, kitchen exhaust fans, bathroom exhaust fans, make up air ducts, HRV's,[3] ERV's,[4] central vacuum cleaners, and powered attic fans.

---

[1] *Air trapped in soil voids or cracks*
[2] http://www.slcc.edu/tech/techsp/asch/courses/ARCH1210/Lecture/Vapotbar/airflow.htm

Example 1:

A West Virginia home was being depressurized by continual dryer usage. The house never had problems until the home went under renovation. New exterior insulation and siding was installed. The contractor also covered all the gable vents with insulation. This home was now tight. The dryer was located in the basement next to a very large crawl space. The crawl space had an exposed soil floor with many cracks in the foundation. The home was also built into a hillside with the crawl being buried. The dryer sucked the moisture out of this crawl and caused upper levels of humidity. The result was mold in closets, on attic sheathing, and on basement joists. We cannot blame the entire contamination on the dryer, due to other variables that were contributors. The client went into her attic and cut a gable vent to help equalize the home pressure and provide more attic ventilation.

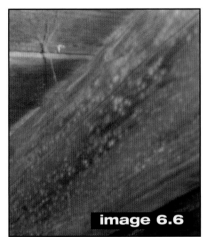

image 6.6

image 6.7

Vapor Diffusion

Vapor diffusion is the movement of moisture that is mixed in air through building materials. Vapor diffusion can move into the building from the exterior. Vapor diffusion can move out of the building from the interior. Vapor diffusion only occurs, when there is a pressure difference in walls or on either side of the building materials. No pressure differences in walls; no vapor diffusion. When buildings are heated in cooled climates, the vapor pressure is higher inside the building that the outside. This means that the vapor pressure will travel from the interior to the exterior. The problem occurs when this vapor diffusion condition causes the moisture to condensate within the interstitial wall cavities. Similarly, when buildings are cooled in warm climates, the vapor pressure is higher on the outside the building than that of the inside. This means that the vapor pressure will travel from the exterior to the interior. The problem once again occurs when this vapor diffusion condition causes the moisture to condensate within the interstitial wall cavities. The following are several examples when vapor diffusion occurs:

Example 2:

Brick wall that gets wet after rain

This is an example of how mold gets behind the vinyl wallpaper. This condition is very common and found in many hotels, high-rise office buildings, and dwellings. For example, let us assume that it rained in the morning and the sun came out in the afternoon. The testing was done in the afternoon after the sun had been out for some time.

- Outside temperature is 80°F. It just rained and the RH is 75 percent. Using the psychrometric chart, the vapor pressure is roughly .68 inches of mercury.
- Inside the room, the temperature is 75°F. the RH is 60 percent. Using the psychrometric chart, the vapor pressure is roughly .54 inches of mercury.
- NOTE: Notice the vapor pressure is slightly higher on the exterior than the interior. This means that the force direction of the vapor will travel from the exterior to the interior. In the illustration, this would be left to right.

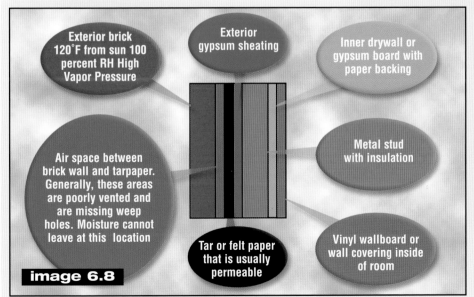

Exterior brick 120°F from sun 100 percent RH High Vapor Pressure

Exterior gypsum sheating

Inner drywall or gypsum board with paper backing

Air space between brick wall and tarpaper. Generally, these areas are poorly vented and are missing weep holes. Moisture cannot leave at this location

Metal stud with insulation

Tar or felt paper that is usually permeable

Vinyl wallboard or wall covering inside of room

image 6.8

The difference between the exterior and interior conditions is rather small. However, the brick (first membrane) will absorb heat and become heated to 120° F. Due to the rain, the brick is wet and RH is 100 percent. This value is so high that it is off the psychrometric chart. You need to go to the steam charts that engineers use. The higher the vapor pressure the higher the driving vapor force pushing it. Significant and adverse conditions will occur. In most buildings, the air space behind the brick is not generally ventilated. The vapor pressure pushes the moisture through this space. By not being ventilated, the moisture and vapor pressure cannot escape. The next membrane (second) is usually felt paper. Most felt products are permeable and will allow vapor pressure to travel through. Many times, large sections of felt are missing or torn or damaged during construction, and vapor will travel quickly through these holes. The next membrane (third) is usually the exterior gypsum sheathing. This is permeable and vapor will travel through. The next membrane (fourth) is the metal stud with fiberglass insulation. This is permeable and vapor will travel through. The next membrane (fifth) is the interior drywall or gypsum board. This is permeable and vapor will travel through. The final membrane (sixth) is vinyl wallpaper. This is not permeable and the vapor stops and condenses. The wall vinyl backing, adhesives, and paper-covered gypsum or drywall interface are nutrients and mold will grow. Mold will digest the adhesives and amplify over time. In some occasions, you will see pink spots on the wallpaper. The pink spots occur when the mold releases digestive enzymes that react with nutrients or cellulose in the wallpaper or the paste.

The problem with this example is the construction design is faulty. The vapor barrier is in the wrong location. The vinyl wallpaper served as the vapor barrier. The vapor barrier should have been placed behind the brick siding or brick veneer.

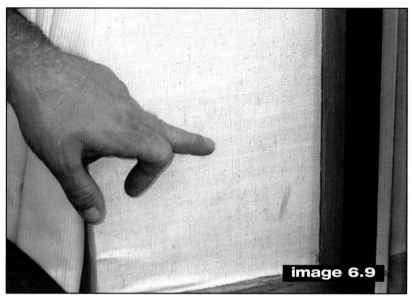

image 6.9

Image 6.9 is a picture of an interior wall in a condominium complex. The unit had vinyl wallpaper on the southeastern side. This unit was on the ninth floor. The odor in the unit was stagnant and slightly musty. A slight pinkish color can be seen in the far-left corner.

Image 6.10 is the same picture of this interior wall with the paper peeled back. Mold reservoirs are amplifying behind the vinyl wallpaper.

image 6.10

SYMPTOMS OF THE ROOM: Pink stains on vinyl wallpaper, loose corners of vinyl wallpaper, stagnant air, musty air, complaints about illness. This example can occur at different temperatures, moisture contents, and vapor pressures.

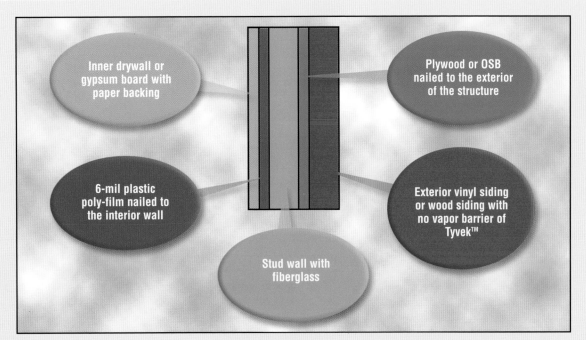

Inner drywall or gypsum board with paper backing

Plywood or OSB nailed to the exterior of the structure

6-mil plastic poly-film nailed to the interior wall

Exterior vinyl siding or wood siding with no vapor barrier of Tyvek™

Stud wall with fiberglass

EXAMPLE 3:

Mixed Climate home with the vapor barrier installed on the warm side.

This is an example of how mold gets behind the six-mil polyethylene plastic inner-wall vapor barrier (Image 6.12). This construction condition is very common in the south. It works better in the south, due to the warmer climate. In the north or in mixed climate areas, this design may have problems.

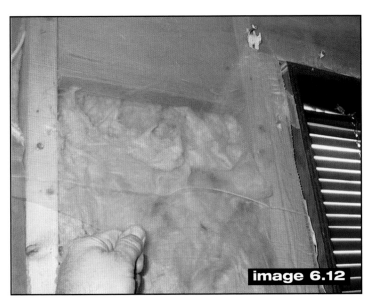

image 6.12

In an air-conditioned home in the summer, the air in the home is cooler than the outdoor air. The interstitial wall cavity will also be cool. If the home is pressurized, the cool air travels to the exterior. The air becomes warmer and warmer, as it moves to the exterior side. This air will eventually infiltrate through random holes. As the infiltrated air gets warmer during its travel, its relative humidity also goes down. Warm air can hold more moisture than cold air, and condensation will not be a factor.

In conclusion, cool air that is escaping due to interior house pressurization will not cause interstitial mold or moisture problems with these conditions. However, if the reverse occurs, a serious condition may occur. We have an attic exhaust fan that is always on in the summer. We also have two eight-inch ducts that travel to a furnace utility room for make-up air purposes. The fan is

image 6.13

image 6.14

sucking air out of the home and out of the utility room. This home is now de-pressurized. Now we are drawing warm, moist, outdoor summer air into the home. This warm moist air is infiltrating into this air-conditioned house. This warm air now is getting cooler as it travels through the interstitial space

image 6.15

Scenario Two

A mixed climate home, summer day with high humidity, air conditioning on, home is depressurized, no six-mil plastic vapor barrier and interior vinyl wallpaper is installed. Now condensation occurs on the backside of the vinyl wallpaper. The vinyl serves as the new vapor barrier and moist air cannot pass through to the interior. This wall is not forgiving. Forgiving walls are better in mixed climate areas.

toward the interior. Remember the drywall is cool, and we have a six-mil vapor barrier. Now the humid air gets cooler during its travel inward and the relative humidity goes up. It stops at the six-mil plastic vapor barrier and condensates. When the condensation becomes excessive, it runs down to the sill plate. The water and moisture eventually cause deterioration.

Image 6.15 is what the six-mil plastic interstitial vapor barrier looks like after you remove the drywall. The inside of the surface of the plastic is where the condensation will occur.

Looking down into the wall cavity you can see the deterioration beginning. Then interstitial inside face of the OSB oriented strand board exterior sheathing wall is also starting to develop mold reservoirs.

Do the math: The temperature indoors is 75° F. The temperature outdoors is 95° F. The outdoor humidity is 70 percent RH. The temperature behind the drywall is 76° F. By using a psychrometric chart, you find the incoming air dew point is 84°F.

image 6.16

Let us now look at a couple different scenarios:

Scenario One

A mixed climate home, summer day with high humidity, air conditioning on, home is depressurized, no six-mil plastic vapor barrier. Now this wall is more forgiving (which is a term used to describe a wall system whereby moist air can easily travel through a wall system without being stopped by a vapor barrier) and moist air can pass through to the interior. Sometimes, forgiving walls are better in mixed climate areas.

Scenario Three

A mixed climate home, winter day, heat on, home is pressurized, no six-mil plastic vapor barrier. Now this wall is more forgiving and moist interior air can pass through to the exterior. When this interior moist air travels to the exterior, it becomes cooler. Now the condensation will occur on the interstitial inner-side of the exterior sheathing (see moisture meter in image 6.16).

Do the math: interior temperature is 69°F., outdoor temperature is 0°F., wall temperature on the drywall is 67°F. The exterior sheathing behind the siding is 9°F. A dew point will form on the inside wall of the exterior sheathing.

SECTION SEVEN
Condition Evaluations

HVAC, DUCTWORK, & MOLD CONCERNING FORCED AIR OR GRAVITY AIR SYSTEMS

The heating, ventilation, and air-conditioning systems (HVAC) in a building is very similar to the respiratory system in a human body. The systems act like a body's blood vessels, routinely distributing conditioned air throughout a building. Drain pans that are built into a system to trap condensate, blower housings, louvers and baffles all can serve as reservoirs of fungal activity.

Energy-conscious building trends began in the 1970s. Now many of these homes have airtight construction with minimal air exchanges. Indoor air can be; old, stagnant, and contaminated. The HVAC system circulates this potential desirable air.

The American Society of Heating, Refrigeration and Air-Conditioning Engineers (ASHRAE) indicates that 50 percent of all cases of poor IAQ and mold contamination result from badly designed, fitted or poorly maintained HVAC systems. HVAC systems can also produce condensation, which contributes to the amplification of fungal reservoirs. Scientific studies have indicated that various types of toxic and nontoxic molds are sometimes present in HVAC systems.

Design specification for HVAC systems should include factors that will minimize moisture accumulation. The HVAC system installed in any building must be well-maintained, inspected, cleaned on a periodic basis, and repaired as needed. Inadequate maintenance may cause amplification and dissemination of non-toxic and toxic molds.

Sources of contamination are HVAC systems

Indoor air quality and mold problems arise in residential buildings when there is inadequate ventilation air provided for the indoor air that contains impurities or contamination. In other words, the home is considered to already have some impurities or contamination, and we do not allow for clean air mixing. The impurities and contamination within the living space brew. The following are the main vehicles that cause indoor air and mold problems:

1. Ventilation inadequate or contaminated exterior air.
2. Inside the HVAC system contamination.
3. Microbial or biological contamination.

Ventilation inadequate

Adequate ventilation can be defined as able to satisfy, suitable for area in question, barely satisfactory for area in question, or sufficient for the area in question. Ventilation air is defined as supposed clean outdoor air brought in to the indoor living area in question. This supposed clean exterior air is exchanged with the exhausted indoor air. The new incoming exterior air is diluted with the indoor air that usually contains some impurities and contamination. The constant process of air dilution is called air exchanges. Air exchanges are necessary in homes to minimize the recirculation on stagnant air.

In some rare cases, the exterior air could be contaminated and now be mixing the exterior. If air exchanges are to be mechanical type, or drawn from intakes to air handling units, placement is very important. Do not place these intakes near stagnant roof puddles, cooling towers, plumbing vents, building exhausts from kitchens or fume hoods, garages or parking garages, loading docks, dumpster areas, trash compactor areas, location were pigeon or bird droppings many exist. These are all impurities and contaminants that will pollute the indoor air.

If mechanical ventilation is not to be used, exterior air comes from opening doors and windows or from boiling depressurization. In one small West Virginia town in August, air was found to contain over 27,0000 Colony Forming Units (CFU) of *Cladosporium* mold spores, the indoor air only contained 4,000 Colony Forming Units (CFU) of *Cladosporium*. This means that every time the door or window is opened, the home fills up with many *Cladosporium* mold spores. If the home has wet, moist, or humid conditions, the *Cladosporium* spores will form fungal reservoirs and amplify. In a Cleveland home, the attic served as a pigeon coup. The owners would open windows on the lower floor directly under the pigeon entrance and exit window. Thousands of other homes throughout the country have urea foam insulation (UFI) in the walls. If the home is depressurized, the UFI out-gas is sucked into the home. Similarly, air from a wet crawl space, that is full of fungal reservoirs, can be sucked into the home during depressurization as well.

Inside contamination

Air pollutants and contamination can arise from the HVAC and ductwork equipment. Within a HVAC system, many locations are susceptible to become contaminated. The outdoor air intake chamber, air filter, condensate drain pan, heat exchanger, supply air fan, duct liner, and other locations are all potential microbial reservoir locations.

The Outdoor air intake chamber

This type of installation may not apply to all residential systems. If the system has an outdoor air intake inlet and chamber, exterior contaminates can enter. As mentioned earlier; do not place these intakes near stagnant roof puddles, cooling towers, plumbing vents, building exhausts from kitchens or fume hoods, garages or parking garages, loading docks, dumpster areas, trash compactor areas, location were pigeon or bird droppings many exist.

HVAC return or conditioned registers

These units can be very contaminated. When we look for microbial contamination in an HVAC system, we will always take a swab sample from a register, diffuser, or vent cover. The visual condition of these units usually are good indicators of what the rest of the system may look like. (See Image 7.1-7.3)

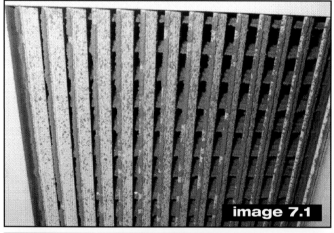

image 7.1

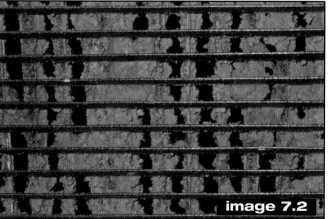

image 7.2

Air filter

Most air filters in buildings and dwellings are poorly maintained. Occupants allow filters to become excessively dirty. Dirty filters produce odors, VOC's and are potential mediums for microbial and bacterial amplification. Additionally dirty or clogged filters will restrict the airflow, increase HVAC maintenance, and cause large pressure drops. The digital image shows a furnace filter to be very dirty. This filter is so dirty that the dust is forming clumps on the filter edges.

image 7.3

Condensate drain pan and evaporator

The evaporator or cooling coil are always wet during the cooling season. During the cooling season, warm air is cooled by passing through the evaporator or cooling coils. Excessive moisture in the warm air is condensed into liquid form when passing through the evaporator or cooling coil. The condensate drips water into the drain pans. The drain pans are used to collect condensate from the evaporator coil during the cooling season. These drain pans are reservoirs and will hold water for long periods. If poorly maintained, these pans become filled with dust, debris, contaminants and other impurities. Now we have a full water reservoir which is a desirable medium for fungal and bacterial contamination. As air moves over this pan and over the wet evaporator or cooling coil, it picks up contaminants and disperses them throughout the home. These pans and cooling coils should be cleaned and inspected every three months.

Heat exchanger

These units are metal and they can rust, corrode, or crack. When these conditions occur, products of combustion leak into the home. These products of combustion may be more serious than any mold condition that may exist.

Supply air fan

The supply fan can be also covered with microbial growth due to the combination of the high humidity downstream of the evaporator, and accumulated debris that has passed by the filters. These contaminants and impurities can adhere to the fan equipment.

Duct liner

Ducts, air handlers, and other HVAC systems are often insulated within fiberglass, glass fiberboard, or other insulation materials. Sometimes, the systems are insulated internally. Internal insulation materials with a rough porous surface will trap particles and contaminants from the passing air stream.

image 7.4

These particles can be plant matter, fibers, asbestos, mold, skin fragments, paper fibers, fungal spores, pollen, grains, plant hairs, mites, carpet fibers, house dust, and other organic matter. These materials are often hygroscopic and can absorb moisture from the passing air stream. When moisture is added to this

image 7.5

condition, it is probable that fungal reservoirs will develop. These fungal reservoirs amplify on these mediums and produce spores that release into the passing air stream. When this insulation is placed on the exterior of the HVAC components, the same condition can occur if duct leakage exists. If the duct leakage is on the return side, then the contaminants come from the HVAC internal system. If the duct leakage is on the supply side then the contaminants come from other building areas or from the exterior. Both of these conditions becomes serious during the cooling season, due to the condensation from the evaporator, the stagnant water in the drain pans, and the latent exterior infiltration of humid air.

image 7.6

Ductwork that is poorly maintained can become contaminated with all types of debris. The Image 7.5 is a grossly contaminated ductwork system in a gaming facility. The dust is so thick that the ductwork was deflecting. The laboratory analysis of this material was found to be mostly carpet fibers, human skin cells, paper, cloth fibers and more. This condition is optimal for insects and fungi.

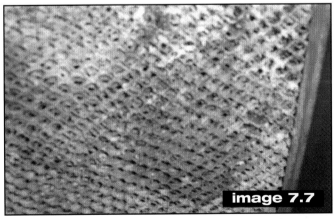

image 7.7

Many older homes have the gravity system or furnace with cold air returns not connected. No return-side ductwork. The famous term called "THE CLEVELAND DROP" is exactly this condition. It was in Cleveland that the early mold studies originated and linked baby deaths and mold. In many of these studies, mold was coming up into the upper home from the basement. The conditioned air somehow has to make it back to the furnace or HVAC system to be recycled. During this journey, the air picks up contaminants from the basement, crawl, floor, confined space or other. The furnace or HVAC system also has to work much harder to heat up this returning air.

In the Image 7.4, the base of the cold air has dead animal hair, bird droppings, moisture, mold, and dust. These contaminants eventually end up in the upper floors. This system is an example of "THE CLEVELAND DROP".

Humidifier

Humidifiers can provide moisture for microbial growth. The Image 7.7 is the inside of a poorly maintained humidifier. Numerous cases of illness were reported because of excessive fungal growth within the humidifiers. Humidifiers can also cause major problems when not properly used. Many residential homeowners leave these units on at the high setting during winter months. Our studies have found that roughly 10 percent of the 1970's and 1980's energy crises homes built in the north, have fungal reservoirs on the north attic side from winter condensation. If ducts leak on the supply side, then moisture from the continually running humidifier will leak into undesirable or interstitial areas, possibly causing fungal reservoirs.

Microbial or biological contamination

Several microbial and biological contaminants can be found in HVAC systems. The main contaminants are fungi and bacteria. These contaminants are usually saprophytes and need nutrients and moisture to survive. In poorly maintained HVAC systems, nutrients and moisture are not hard to find. Other living or dead contaminants that can be found are insects, nematodes and dust mites. These contaminants are usually the result of fungal growth. In many instances, the mold reservoirs can be found attached to the insects. Both fungal and bacterial contamination can produce adverse effects. Fungal contaminants produce allergens, mycotoxins, beta-1, glucans, and fungal volatile organic chemicals (VOC's). Bacterial contamination produces allergenic proteins, endotoxins, bacterial volatile organic chemicals (VOC's).

Often occupants complain about musty odors. Musty odors are generally traced to microbial amplification of fungal reservoirs.

Cooling coils or evaporators have been known to have the following species of fungi; *Acremonium sp., Aureobasidium, Phon spp., Sporobolomyces spp., Rhodotorula spp,* and *yeasts*.

Drain pans, drip pans, and humidifiers have been known to have Gram-negative bacteria and endotoxins.

Ductwork and other HVAC components have been known to have the following fungi; *Cladosporium spp., Cladosporium, Penicillium spp., Penicillium* and *Aspergillus spp.*

Cooling towers have been known to have *Legionella*, a waterborne bacterium. This contaminant is usual found in warm or hot water and can cause Legionnaire's disease and Pontiac fever.

HVAC MAINTENANCE

The HVAC system can cause fungal reservoirs to develop on other homes components. If the furnace is not properly balanced, they can be sucking or depressurizing a certain room. Depressurization can cause infiltration of contaminants, exterior latent moisture, and soil gasses. The following are conditions that can lead to fungal reservoir development due to unbalanced HVAC and / or duct air leakage.

Duct systems loose energy in three ways
1. Conduction of heat through the duct walls, especially if located in cold areas.
2. Pressure differences or pressure drops. Air leakage from the HVAC system; Energy can be lost through leakage of heated air into and out of ducts, through accidental holes in ductwork and through open areas between loosely connected members.
3. Infiltration caused by pressure imbalances. Pressure imbalances caused by faulty ducts will cause air to leak more readily through holes and cracks in the walls or ceilings of the structure. This is known as air infiltration. One example may be that a particular room has a supply register and no return register, or visa versa. Now let us close the door in this room. In the room with no return, the room will act like a balloon being blown up. This room is pressurized and air will want to exfiltrate to the exterior. This will put more burden on the heating system causing energy loss and an unbalanced system. Additionally this may cause depressurizing at other locations. In the other areas where a return exists, the room is depressurized and sucking cold or hot humid air from the exterior, also know as infiltration. This condition will also lead to indoor air pollution and interstitial bio-growth.

Obvious Evidence of Supply & Return-Side Leakage

- Joints not sealed or poorly sealed.
- Dust tape used. Duct tape will loose it adhesiveness after a few years. In return ducts that are insulated, you may see accumulation of soot. Many times, the duct tape is used on the hot flues of exhaust vents. When the exhaust flue of vents get hot, they cause the duct tape to melt, giving off chemical gas.
- Floor penetration between levels. These penetrations could be from HVAC or other mechanical systems. The basement level is most susceptible to this condition. These penetrations allow heated air exfiltration, and cold air to infiltrate during heating seasons. When this happens, the pressure, difference in the basement is likely to increase air infiltration into the basement.

Not-so-Obvious Evidence of Supply & Return-Side Leakage

- Non-insulated ducts in unconditioned spaces. Heat loss is not just from leakage conditions. Conductive heat losses are typically, at least as great. Non-insulated ducts in vented crawls, attics, and exterior outside walls are some of these conditions.
- Disconnected, torn, plugged, or damaged ducts. Examples may include; connections that have become loose, torn insulation on flexible ducts, or damaged fiberglass duct boards from weight that may have been placed on them. When flexible ducts are bent, damaged, or have unnecessary bends, they restrict the air flow and cause pressure drops.
- Blind alley ducts. These conditions are sometimes found in duct systems that use joist spaces or other parts of the building structure to move air flow. Blind alley ducts usually occur because of mistakes made during construction installation. These blind alley ducts generally lead nowhere. Sometimes, these blind alley ducts lead to the exterior. When registers feel cold or you do not realize any air flow, these conditions should be investigated. Raising the thermostat to get one room warmer is not the solution.
- Missing return-side ductwork. Many older homes have this condition. The famous term mentioned earlier "THE CLEVELAND DROP" is exactly this condition. The conditioned air has to somehow make it back to the furnace to be recycled. The furnace has to work much harder to heat up this returning air due to it being surrounded by generally cooler air. These systems are also generally unbalanced.

Do I have a problem with my HVAC system?

- Which room is the warmest at 4:00 in the afternoon? They all feel the same at 4:00 PM. (*Air is out of balance. Perform air testing and balancing, and duct renovation procedures.*)
- Do you have registers or grills that make excessive noise? (*Excessive air velocity. Increase register or grill size, or add another duct run.*)
- Does steam collect on your bathroom mirror after a bath or shower? (*Inadequate exhaust. Install larger fan and balance.*)
- Does your home get dusty within two days after dusting? (*Poor indoor air quality and duct leakage. Duct leakage testing, indoor air quality testing, and total supply and return air testing needed.*)
- Do you have to turn up your TV when the fan comes on? (*Excessive velocity or refrigerant leak. Add new grills or increase registers.*)
- Does your air conditioner or heater run continuously without adequately heating or cooling? (*Duct leakage or refrigerant leak. Test with airflow hood and test refrigerant charge.*)
- Is your condensing unit or furnace loud at night? (*Sound testing. Poor compressor insulation. Old unit. Damaged fan. Insulate, relocate, repair, or replace. Install isolation pads or compressor jacket.*)
- Have you had continuous problems with your system since it was installed? (*Poor quality installation. System commissioning or system review with prescription writing.*)
- Do your windows collect condensation on the inside? Does mold or mildew grow? *Hot and cold spots throughout. Comfort balancing, thermostat*

Many of the above conditions can cause undesirable outcomes. Air quality in your home is important for a clean and healthy environment. Poor air quality can make people sick, damage the home, and make other systems fail.

You should perform inspections periodically and maintain the HVAC system on regular bases. The following are some maintenance tips that would help in diminishing microbial fungal reservoirs a fungal amplification.

Some maintenance tips of HVAC systems

- Ensure adequate filtration - most homes have two-dollar throwaway filters. These filters should be changed every month. If you have an electronic filter, it should be cleaned every two months. If you have a HEPA or SPACE GUARD filter, you should change it every 6 months. Dirty environments require more frequent filter changes. Do not install a larger size, HEPA, or high density medium filter on your furnace without first checking the pressure drop. You may damage the HVAC system. Many times when occupants change filters to be more efficient, adjustments must be made to the fan, pulley or electric motor.
- Routinely inspect interior equipment for signs of corrosion or rusting. This maintenance should be done monthly. When you find moisture and corrosion, you must identify the source.
- Clean condensate pans before cooling; wash with diluted 0.5 or 50% bleach solution or other acceptable product.
- Inspect condensate overflow pans for corrosion or rust. This should be done monthly. When you find corrosion or rust you must identify the source.
- Ensure adequate insulation of refrigerant and condensate lines.
- Properly insulate ducting in attics, crawls or cold areas.
- Prevent air leakage into and out of HVAC systems.
- Turn gas pilot lights off in summer when applicable. In some cases it is beneficial to leave them on because it keeps the heat exchanger from condensating and rusting.
- Give immediate attention to signs of visible condensation on and around HVAC systems, including supply vents, suction lines or other components.
- Moisture on the floor or under the HVAC unit. You should also look for moisture stains under the HVAC unit. Stains are indications of past leaks or condensation. The condensation may only occur at certain times.
- Shut chimney dampers when not in use. Chimney tops shall also have animal screens.
- Make random inspections and eliminate damaging pests in the attic, crawl or location.
- Maintain proper standards for conditioning of inside air (73° F in the summer, and 68-73° F in the winter with 30% to 60% relative humidity.) Be very careful when using the humidifier.
- Properly balance the entire HVAC system.
- Do not store items on HVAC ducts that might damage them.
- At minimum, have an annual inspection of the home by qualified HVAC contractor knowledgeable in microbial issues.

Balancing your heating system

We recommend that technicians be certified by the NCI, NEBB, or AABC when performing the following work. The following items should be expected of a certified air balancer - gather design information and prepare reports.

The following information was provided by the NATIONIAL COMFORT INSTITUTE located at: 4259 Sheffield Lake, Ohio 44054, 1-800-633-7058.

Psychrometrics and dew point projections

Water can enter buildings from roof, wall, foundation, doors, or window leaks. Leaking pipes, floods, sewer back-ups, and water accidents are also sources of water entry. We call these conditions significant events and unless the resulting water is not removed quickly, there is likely to be mold growth on optimum mediums.

Even more complex is mold development associated with moisture that condenses out of the air. All air contains moisture or grains of moisture. The moisture holding capacity of air is dependent on temperature. Warmer air can hold more moisture, or grains of moisture, than that of cold air. When air cools or loses heat, it will hold less moisture. Engineers have designed a chart called the psychrometric chart. A psychrometric chart graphically illustrates the relationships between air temperature and relative humidity as well as other properties. This psychrometric chart can be used for many applications. For our purpose, we will only use this chart for dew points and simple mold applications. We have simplified this chart for this book's application. We will only be interested in four different variables: wet bulb temperature, dry bulb temperature, dew point, and relative humidity. We will show the relationship that by knowing dew point, we can predict mold or explain amplifications.

We will first define these four variables for your understanding.

• Wet-Bulb Temperature

Wet-bulb temperature reflects the cooling effect of evaporating water (like drying your hands in one of those public bathroom wall-push-button air dryers). Wet-bulb temperature can be determined by passing air over a thermometer that has been wrapped with a small amount of moist fabric. The cooling effect of the evaporating water causes a lower temperature compared to the dry-bulb ambient air temperature. The wet-bulb temperature scale is located along the curved upper left portion of the chart on page 27. The sloping lines indicate equal wet-bulb temperatures.

• Dry-Bulb Temperature

Dry-bulb temperature is the air temperature determined by an ordinary thermometer. The dry-bulb temperature scale is located at the base of the chart. Vertical lines indicate constant dry-bulb temperature. The weatherman uses this unit for temperature.

• Relative Humidity

Relative humidity is a measure of how much moisture is present compared to how much moisture the air could hold at that temperature. Relative humidity is expressed as a percent. Lines representing conditions of equal relative humidity's sweep (happy smile curve) from the lower left to the upper right of the psychrometric chart. The 100 percent relative humidity (saturation) line corresponds to the wet-bulb and the dew point temperature scale line. (This is the happy smile last curve on the far left side). The line for zero percent relative humidity falls along the dry-bulb temperature scale line. Relative humidity is the unit that weathermen use in their weather reporting.

By knowing only two of the three above variables, we can predict dew point and visually graph it. This dew point will allow us to predict or explain mold growth.

• Dew Point Temperature

Dew point temperature is the temperature below that value which moisture will condense out of the air. Air that is holding as much water vapor as possible is saturated, or at its dew point. Water will condense on a surface, such as a building wall, attic sheathing, basement foundation, or pitcher of ice water that is at or below the dew point temperature of the air. The dew point temperature scale is located along the same curved portion of the chart as the wet-bulb temperature scale. However, horizontal lines indicate equal dew point temperatures. The dew point can also be read on the far left-hand side of the chart. I like to draw a horizontal line all the way to this far left-hand side. This entire horizontal line is the dew point that never changes, only the temperature changes. You can also draw this line horizontally to the far left-hand side and dew point will still remain the same. Air will only hold so much moisture, the warmer the air the more the moisture it will hold. As air cools, it will hold less moisture. This moisture is also called grains of water in the air.

It is this dew point we are trying to determine. If we know the dew point, then we can predict mold or at least know why the mold grew here and not there. If we understand dew point, we can alter it and stop potential mold reservoirs from forming. We will apply this concept to an example. You will need to know at least two variables to determine the dew point. You can

purchase a sling psychrometer and spin it for three minutes, to get the wet and dry-bulb temperatures. It is very easy to use. This will give enough data to use the psychrometric chart to find the dew point. We like using electronic gauges because they automatically tell the dew point. These gauges can be purchased for less than one hundred dollars. So now, you ask, "Why then do you need this fancy, difficult-looking chart?" You do not, but the color chart looks great on reports. What it does do, is once you plot your points you can see a bigger picture and make projections and conclusions when condensation could or have occurred. If you have a litigation matter, you'll want to use the sling psychrometer and psychrometric chart. The sling will never be wrong, unlike electronic gauges that may have deviations. The psychrometric chart will always be right, unlike your calculator when you press the wrong button.

EXERCISE ONE

The readings occurred in the living room of a slab home in the summer months. The ceiling in this room had odd long narrow moisture stains that resembled pool table stick marks. Where did these stains come from?

From your sling psychrometer, you have a dry-bulb (DB) of 68° F. and wet-bulb (WB) of 64° F. What is the dew point?

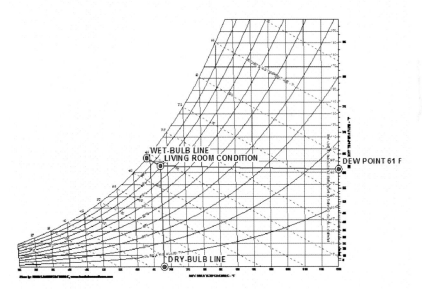

From the chart, the dew point is 61° F. This means that any surface that has a temperature of 61° F will start to condensate. If you were to water your grass with city water, the copper cold water line would eventually reach ground temperature. The ground temperature is 55° F for this geographical area. As the cold water runs through this pipe, the pipe gets cold and starts to condensate. If the insulation on your air conditioning suction line is damaged, it would start to condensate. The stains for this example are from pipes that are condensating above the living room ceiling in the interstitial space.

You need to lower this interstitial space dew point. You can do this in two ways. The obvious is to remove the grains of moisture through de-humidification, or increase the air temperature in the home. Beware of sprinkler system piping above the ceiling. These pipes can cause tremendous condensation especially if left on for long periods.

EXERCISE TWO

From your laser infrared gauge, you obtain a basement foundation surface wall temperature of 55°F. These gauges can be bought for about one hundred dollars. From your thermometer, you read a basement room temperature of 76°F. The basement walls have mold in the corners and on the base of the foundation walls. What is the humidity of the basement? In what season did this mold condition most likely occur?

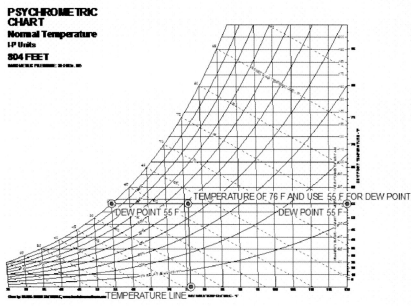

From the chart, the relative humidity is 48.1 percent. In this question, you can assume that the wall temperature is the dew point because the wall felt wet to the touch. The wall temperature is also at the ground temperature with 55°F for this geographical area. It is difficult to answer the second part of the question. If the temperature drops during cooling season, the humidity will automatically increase and the dew point would still be 55°F. If the temperature increases during heating, then the humidity will decrease and the dew point would still be 55°F.

The solution to this example is to dehumidify and remove grains of moisture out of the air.[1]

Example of Attic Mold on the north side of a Home: Part One

We have an older Cleveland home. The home is rented by tenants who are frugal and will not run a dehumidifier because it costs money. (Humidifiers usually cost about $15-$30/month). They claim they are sick and have short-term memory loss due to supposed mold in the attic. The landlord calls you to investigate the condition, to figure out this mess.

You go to the home and make the following observations:

1. The furnace has a humidifier that is constantly on. This is a common problem with most homes that have humidifiers. People do not understand that you cannot leave these units on continuously all winter in northern states. You must adjust these units as the exterior temperature changes.

2. The basement has some moisture stains on the older foundation. These stains are white in color, and you will assume that some foundation infiltration exists.

3. The attic ventilation is restricted by insulation stuffed into the soffits.

4. The sling psychrometer reads 48°F dry-bulb and 40.5°F wet-bulb temperature in the attic. With these two values, you read the humidity level from the sling at 52%. This is high humidity for an attic in the winter.

While in the attic, we see this black mold predominantly on the north side. This mold is only on the attic sheathing and not on the joists. You plot the 48° F attic temperature and the 52 percent humidity values on the chart and determine a dew point temperature of 31.3°F. This is the magical number that will cause condensation or frost on the attic sheathing. You use your handy laser thermometer and test the surface temperature of the sheathing and find it to be 33°F. Remember that the sheathing surface temperature is different than the attic air temperature. This value is not a problem now because it is lower than 31.3°F. You go back downstairs and you hear the television newsman say that the temperature will drop 10 degrees tonight. Now you have a problem, because later that evening the attic sheathing will be at a lower temperature than the calculated dew point temperature. The humidity in the attic will cause condensation, and the attic sheathing will become covered by frost. This frost will

---

[1] For further information contact us at our website www.forensicinspection.com

vaporize in the morning when the sun comes out and get absorbed into the wood sheathing. Mold will form on this wet cellulose product. You look at the meteorological charts and you find out the average temperature for the coldest month in Cleveland is 28° F plus or minus 6° F which is lower than the dew point (22° F -34° F). Most roof sheathing is generally only 1/2 to 5/8 inch thick. This means, that this attic has the potential to have numerous events occur. If you are good, you can actually calculate how many times these events may have occurred, as long as you know at least two of the variables.

Go to your local lumber supply store and buy a dehumidifier. Place this dehumidifier in the basement to help out with the basement wall moisture condition. Turn the dehumidifier on and leave the home. Three days later, you come back and retest the attic. The values still have the same 48° F dry-bulb, but the humidity had lowered to 32 percent due to the humidifier removing grains of water. Plot the dew point, and find out it is now 20.9° F. You just solved the attic mold problem.

The following is the graphical representation of the above example. Programs exist which you can purchase that do the graphing for you.[2]

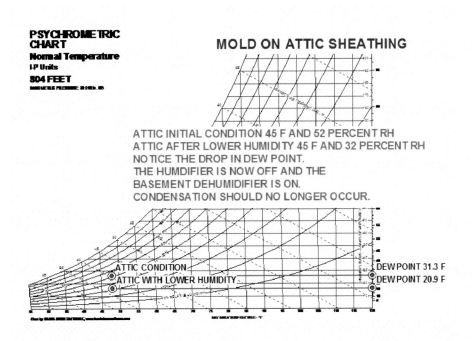

PSYCHROMETRIC CHART
Normal Temperature
I-P Units
804 FEET

MOLD ON ATTIC SHEATHING

ATTIC INITIAL CONDITION 45 F AND 52 PERCENT RH
ATTIC AFTER LOWER HUMIDITY 45 F AND 32 PERCENT RH
NOTICE THE DROP IN DEW POINT.
THE HUMIDIFIER IS NOW OFF AND THE
BASEMENT DEHUMIDIFIER IS ON.
CONDENSATION SHOULD NO LONGER OCCUR.

ATTIC CONDITION
ATTIC WITH LOWER HUMIDITY

DEW POINT 31.3 F
DEW POINT 20.9 F

Chart shows the dew point was lowered by simply turning off the humidifier on the furnace.
A dehumidifier was also added to the basement.

---

[2] See acknowledgments for the program information do determine psychrometrics

Same Example: Part Two

Tell the homeowner that high humidity is the cause of the attic mold. Also, tell the landlord that it is not entirely his fault that the mold amplified in the attic. It is also the tenant's fault because the tenant left the humidifier on continually. The landlord asks, "Can I take any other precautions, other than running a basement dehumidifier and turning off the furnace humidifier"? The answer is yes, we could add more ventilation to the attic. We can also recalculate the new dew point. We remove the insulation from the soffit vents, and we add a continuous ridge vent.

Now the attic is being vented with exterior air. We come back to the home three days after the attic ventilation is installed. We still have the same temperature but the wet bulb or humidity is now different. It is different because the exterior humidity levels will now will mix with the attic humidity levels. Knowing exactly what the percentage of exterior air mixing, is difficult to determine. For this example, we will use a fifty-fifty mix. The exterior temperature is 28° F. with a humidity of 27%. The attic temperature is still 45° F. with the initially lowered humidity of 32%. Plot these values and look at the chart.

This chart shows the dew point was lowered even more by simply adding exterior air through ventilation that contained lower humidity. We did not provide the mixing formula. This example shows you that the dew point will drop even lower when ventilation is added to the attic. (Summer months are different).

By using psychrometrics and charting, one can graphically predict the amount of water that will be available to the location. This information is crucial in determining the source of moisture at a location and identifying the potential of microbial growth.

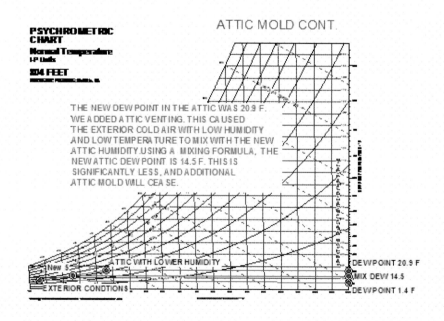

ATTIC MOLD CONT.

PSYCHROMETRIC CHART
Normal Temperature
I-P Units
304 FEET

THE NEW DEW POINT IN THE ATTIC WAS 20.9 F. WE ADDED ATTIC VENTING. THIS CAUSED THE EXTERIOR COLD AIR WITH LOW HUMIDITY AND LOW TEMPERATURE TO MIX WITH THE NEW ATTIC HUMIDITY. USING A MIXING FORMULA, THE NEW ATTIC DEW POINT IS 14.5 F. THIS IS SIGNIFICANTLY LESS, AND ADDITIONAL ATTIC MOLD WILL CEASE.

DEW POINT 20.9 F
MIX DEW 14.5
DEW POINT 1.4 F

ATTIC WITH LOWER HUMIDITY
EXTERIOR CONDITIONS

SECTION EIGHT

Ductwork Problems and Mold

PROBLEMS WITH DUCTWORK UNDERNEATH SLABS

Many homes have ductwork in and under their slabs. This is common practice in many states. Most people overlook these installations as far as their potential for IAQ problems. If overlooked, these can be major contributors to indoor air problems and ruined homes.

This is a system that was very common in the 1940-1970's. Many builders used the same clay pipe that they used for underground drains. Many times, the joints are dry fitted and allow debris or moisture to enter.

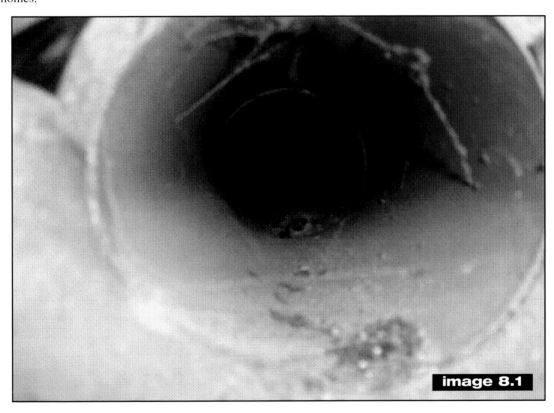

image 8.1

Practical data collection using a digital camera:

You start out by taking out your new small digital camera. You need to stay focused and do this in order. Take the first digital photograph of the register and record your data. Now you know where you started. Take the register cover off. Take your second digital image. Now stick your hand into the ductwork, and position the camera so the camera is looking down the ductwork, then snap your third digital image. For your fourth image, turn the camera one hundred eighty degrees. Now the camera is aimed in the opposite direction. Snap your last image. Now you have four digital images of one duct location. Move clock-wise to the next duct and repeat. If you have problems with opening the register at one location, put your hand in view of the camera with your thumb pointing down. You will recognize this as not accessible. Now plug your camera into your computer. You can zoom in on your images and look into ductwork. Your digital camera can be an investigation tool. You can look at the images and you will see where you need to re-take additional photos. The following are some duct systems under slabs that have problems.

In the clay duct (Image 8.1), you can see a lighter or dirty half moon arc on the lower half of the duct. This is a moisture stain. This duct was flooded at one time. It appears as if only one flood had occurred. Generally, you would see different levels of staining, like looking at the annual rings of a tree. This can be interpreted as irregular installation. The builder allowed water to enter the duct system during construction.

Image 8.2 is of a condominium utilizing metal ducts for corners and composite ducts for runs. In this duct you can see that water intrusion occurred. The heavy build up of dirt and mold is an indication of an ongoing leaking problem. From photographs such as this you are able to determine the source of water intrusion. The occupant would sneeze every time the furnace would kick on when she occupied this room.

This dirt is hard to clean and a duct cleaner will not do a good job here. Show the duct-cleaning technician this image, and he will make sure he works extra hard at this area.

Image 8.3 was taken in a new home. We were doing a punch list inspection for the new prospective buyer. The following are some conditions that may require re-negotiation.

image 8.2

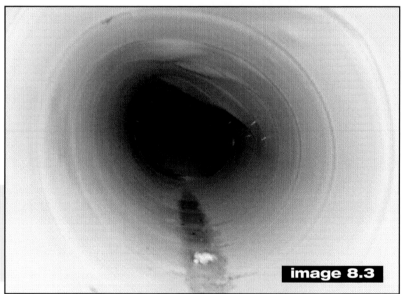

image 8.3

1. Water in the ductwork. Direct result of poor construction practice.
2. Damaged ductwork from men stepping on ducts during concrete slab placement.
3. Debris in the ducts.

These are all conditions that are not acceptable for new home construction.

Notice the fastener nail ends that stick into the system. These can cause problems to duct cleaning companies.

This type of ductwork is a flexible plastic type. These types of ducts were common in the 1970-1980. Several problems exist with these ducts.

1. They can easily crush under pressure.
2. Dust and moisture can get trapped in the grooves. You cannot clean these properly. Mold can amplify on dust and dirt within these small grooves. If you add up all the square area of uncleaned grooves that may contain mold, it is significant.

This is not a desired product to use underground for heating ductwork. This material is common for exterior use or landscaping drainage.

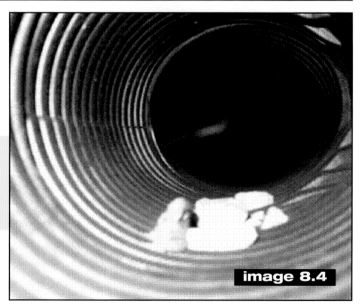

image 8.4

Note in Image 8.4, the stones that are located in the center of this duct. This is aggregate used under the slab. No aggregate, or any construction debris for that matter, should be found within the duct system.

Image 8.5 is a clay pipe duct utilized as in-slab duct work. The biggest problem with these systems is that they crack, fall apart, and settle. When this happens, the following conditions occur:

1. Soil from under the slab enters the home.
2. Moisture from under the slab enters the ducts.
3. Odors can emanate from substrate materials.
4. Water can flood these areas.
5. Broken tiles will fall into the duct and restrict the airflow. It is very hard to fix this problem. We consider this to be a major defect in a home.

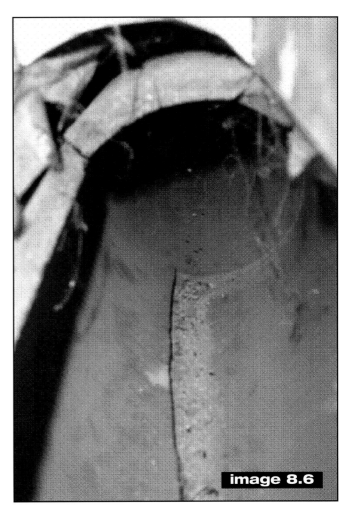

image 8.6

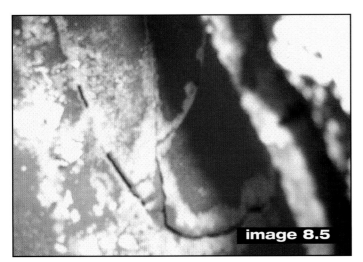

image 8.5

The white plastic new ducts seen in Image 8.7 are harder to inspect. The flash of your camera reflects on the white walls and produces a very light-colored photograph. What sometimes works is to place your thumb over part of the flash and try to restrict some of it. In this photo, a trained eye will still see a flood mark and some debris at the bottom of the duct.

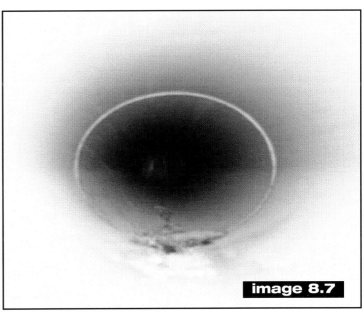

image 8.7

This clay system in Image 8.8 is actively flooded. You can see the dirty water in the ductwork. This dirty water is actually being pulled out of the soil that exists under the slab. If you look closely you will also notice several old flood marks.

This problem cannot be repaired. Too many variables have to be addressed. The easiest repair is to fill in the ducts with concrete and re-route new ductwork overhead.

Water in the ductwork is a serious problem. The water reservoir will allow mold and bacteria to grow inside the network. When the furnace or AC is turned on, the water will be evaporated into the home causing high humidity. High humidity means dew points, condensation, and mold. High humidity in the home will also cause dust mites to thrive and cause sensitized or immune compromised people to become sick.

image 8.8

Clean ducts mean no mold!

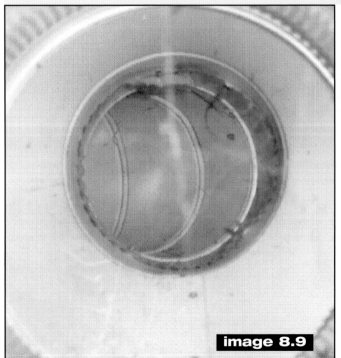
image 8.9

image 8.10

SECTION NINE

The Spore Chart

A SAMPLE SPORE CHART

After the entire battery of test results is completed, it is very important to develop a chart that graphically depicts the fungal conditions at each of the test locations. There are laboratories that will compare in their reports, the difference between the clean air and the test location on Air-O-Cells.

Once we have the results from the tape lifts, the Air-O-Cells, the Swabs and the Anderson plates, we then chart them and graph them.

This process gives a vivid pictorial representation of the fungal or lack of fungal contamination at the test site locations.

This process is also used to compare the results of the post abatement test that are usually taken forty-eight hours after the debris has been removed from the project.

The charting can also include information such as particle density, pollen, skin fragments, fibrous glass and smuts or rusts.

Once the charting is completed and the graphs are made the trained professional can now make decisions based on the information listed.

Along with the Spore chart and the particle chart, photomicrographs are also used to provide pictorial information of the test site and the results that are processed.

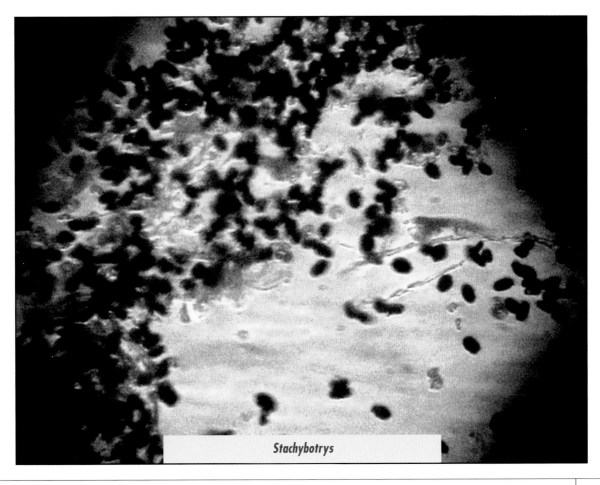

Stachybotrys

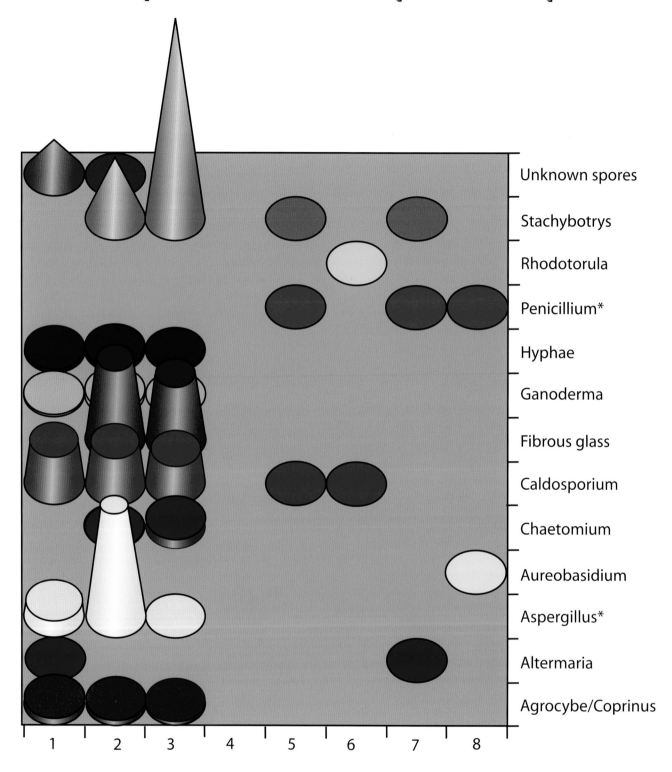

Unknown spores
Stachybotrys
Rhodotorula
Penicillium*
Hyphae
Ganoderma
Fibrous glass
Caldosporium
Chaetomium
Aureobasidium
Aspergillus*
Altermaria
Agrocybe/Coprinus

1   2   3   4   5   6   7   8

Aspergillus and *Penicillium* are small and spherical with very few distinguishing characteristics. They may be counted together (see Air-o-cell guidelines for interpretations in the general comments sections).

*Comparsion sheet of mold spore colony concentration without adjustment of "clean air concentration." This chart is for comparison of location or area concentrations only.

Comparative Spore Chart

L.t.B.   EQL

C = Colonies
C/m³ = Counts per cubic meter

Mold Type	Clean Air C/m³	2nd Level C/m³	1st Level C/m³		Bedroom C	Attic C	Den C	Wood in Bmt C	Clean Air PAT C/m³	2nd Level PAT C/m³	Basement PAT C/m³
Alternaria	82						Yes				
Arthrinium											
Ascomycete											
Aspergillus*	738	5005	>24615								183
Aureobasidium								Yes			
Basidiomycete											
Chaetomium		82	492								
Cladosporium	1969	1887	1559		Yes	Yes					366
Curvularia											
Epicoccum											
Fibrous glass		3610	2954								457
Ganoderma	82	246	82								91
Hyphae	164	246	82								
Mucor											
Paecilomyces											
Penicillium*					Yes		Yes	Yes			
Periconia											
Pithomyces											
Pollen											
Rhizopus											
Rhodotorula						Yes					
Skin fragments											
Stachybotrys		2790	9108		Yes		Yes				
Stemphyllium											
Teliomycetes											
Torula											
Trichoderma											
Trichophyton											
Ulocladium											
Unknown spores	1559	903							46	91	
Uredinales											

These results are indicated for the locations sampled & the time the sample was taken ONLY.
Conditions & concentrations change constanly.

Fibrous glass is in particles per cubic foot or ppcf
N.D. is None Detected
L.t.B. is Less than Background
G.t.B. is Greater than Background

< symbol means less than the amount listed
> symbol means greater than the amount listed

SECTION TEN

The Particle Chart

AIR-BORNE PARTICULATE

Particle Contamination

This is a typical report template that we use. There are several sections that have interchangeable words or phrases. We edit these for each individual particle assessment. There is no appendix to be referenced, as it is in the rear of our microbial investigation report system already.

Scope and Purpose: Use a laser particle counter to sample the air in various locations of the dwelling and determine if there is contamination by airborne particulate; also, to qualify the size and quantify the amounts of the contamination.

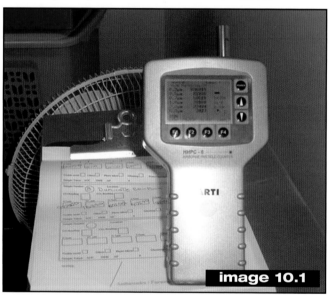

image 10.1

Laser particle count examination is critical to indoor air quality investigations. A particle investigation is designed to quantify air contamination by particle size. Particle counting effectively analyzes the effectiveness of the air handling filtration systems. The device used for this project was an HHPC-6 ARTI Particle counter. Periodic calibration of these units per the manufacturer's recomendations, is imperative. The device has six channels to read various size particles in microns. The channel sizes are .3, .5, .7, 1.0, 2.0, and 5.0. There is a various pump rate, which was set to pump 2.83 liters per minute. This is equal to a volume 1/10th of a cubic foot. The device also indicates relative humidity and temperature.

In the area of indoor air quality, particle counts and contamination are critical to identify whether installed filtration systems are properly functioning. The device quantifies particle contamination and allows the indoor air environmentalist to make determinations based on the results. The device was used in the dwelling to establish contamination in a random and varied amount of locations throughout the contaminated livable and non-livable areas; i.e. the attic or crawl areas, if accessible.

In the appendix, there is a *Comparative Particle and Data Chart*. It identifies locations and counts inclusive of CO, CO_2, if requested relative humidity, temperature, and odor readings. There is a distinct correlation between respiratory penetration and particle size. The symptoms and health affects of particulate inhalations vary from respiratory irritation, allergies, infections, and cancer. In general, respired particles affect us in the following ways:

- They can impair respiratory functions.
- Particles may cause a chemical or mechanical irritation of tissues. Nerve endings at the deposition site can also be damaged.
- They can aggravate existing respiratory or cardiovascular disease. They can impact our immune system and cause more morphological changes in lung tissue.

Health exposure to contaminate falls into two categories. Indoor air quality exposure (which is non-occupational) and occupational. Wallace (1991) and Wilkins (1993) showed that inhaling particles is associated with increased prevalence of "sick building syndrome". The symptoms are mucus irritation, difficulty in concentration, and distraction of occupancy by annoyance odors. Particulate contamination breaks down as follows in the human body, by size, where um is :

- >10, um may be respirable, but does not penetrate
- 7 to 11 um particles penetrate nasal passages
- 4.7 to 7 um particles penetrate the pharynx
- 3.3 to 4.7 um particles penetrate trachea and primary bronchi
- 2.1 to 3.3 um particles penetrate secondary bronchi
- 1.1 to 2.1 um particles penetrate terminal bronchi
- 0.65 to 1.1 um particles penetrate bronchioli
- 0.43 to 0.65 um particles penetrate alveoli

Studies of high-rise office buildings (Armstrong, Sherertz, and Llewellyn, 1989) showed that high levels of particulate resulted in sinus and upper respiratory congestion and headaches. In 1993, Gravessen, Ipsen, and Skov found that macromolecular organic dust correlated significantly with the number of occupant's complaints consisting of:

- Extreme fatigue
- Itching eyes
- Nasal congestion
- Headaches
- Sore and irritated throats

Two categories of particles are of particular concern: microbial and combustion by-product. Microbial particulate causes irritation, allergenic illness, infectious illness, and has toxic effects on the body. Combustion by-products (that is particulate from vehicle exhaust, tobacco smoke, heating appliances, office machinery, and cooking appliances) creates polycyclic aromatic hydrocarbons or PAH's.

Particulate testing is particularly critical to ASHRAE Standard 52.2-1999, titled "Method of Testing General Ventilation Air-Cleaning Devices for Removal Efficiency by Particle Size."[1]

The system's HVAC components observed need to be cleaned, and any debris or visible mold removed. Comment specifically to the indoor air contamination.

Readings were taken of outside air to establish a baseline. We are also comparing the readings to charts of clean rooms and classrooms.[2] The general observation of counting the particle was that there were many irregular and unequal conditions relating to air quality.

The following are Conclusions to be drawn from the Air Particle Testing:

1. There is (significant, limited, very sparse) contamination of the air in multiple areas tested, and the dwelling in general, by airborne particulate.
2. The filters and filtration system is not functioning to filter the airborne particulate.
3. Contamination is coming for an internal source, such as the amplified growth and spore activity on the wall surfaces and in the cabinets, or an internal unidentified source, i.e., behind the dry wall, or from the water-filled floor ducts.
4. All areas of the dwelling show unacceptable levels of particle contamination, i.e. microbial activity or dust. The physical complaints of occupants correlate to the high particulate counts recorded.

Recommendations Regarding This Information:

- The sources of the airborne particulate should be identified and mitigated.
- Review the recommendations in the mold report.
- The document ACR 2002 Assessment, Cleaning & Restoration of HVAC Systems should be purchased and reviewed. The National Air Duct Cleaners Association publishes this document: NADCA. Their recommended procedures should be used and guidelines followed.
- If you are an immune-compromised individual, proper air scrubbing apparatus should be used to clean the particulate contamination in your dwelling. Portable air scrubbers are available.
- We are not health specialists. The conclusions and opinions stated in this report are based on information gathered over time and the review of similar situations and conditions.

---

[1] Standards and Appendix
[2] See "Airborne Particulate Class Chart"

Comparative Particle & Data Chart

EQL

Test Type* Laser Particle Counts Is In Microns	0.3um	0.5um	0.7um	1.0um	2.0um	5.0um	CO	CO$_2$	%RH	TEMP	ODOR
LOCATIONS											
Outside Air	10213	88	474	321	171	15			37	72	
22808 Conference	8194	1080	680	529	329	64			44	72	
2202 Jones	8165	676	345	227	119	16			44	70	
Mens Room	7530	639	324	208	99	6			43	73	
2223 Shana	11337	2935	2115	1663	1016	183			42	73	
2222/2258 Linda	9267	1454	903	681	396	60			41	74	
2280 Ron	9935	1435	846	597	317	42			37	73	
2211 Marc	8450	976	562	401	223	29			40	73	
Managers Station	6876	1009	646	494	301	63			40	75	
Kitchen	7583	017	605	427	230	30			41	75	
2251/2214 Fk & Db	8541	1107	649	459	243	33			41	74	
Mailroom	7378	748	368	237	112	9.5			40	72	
Computer Rm	7611	537	218	135	56	3.2			40	72	
Completed Files	10649	1147	626	456	262	44			39	74	
Shipping	35731	3406	1787	1349	828	14			38	72	
Vault Room	13146	1677	969	693	371	44			39	73	
Ladies Rm	15640	1060	387	230	100	9.5			39	72	
Boiler Rm	10732	948	451	312	166	20			38	74	
2260 Dan	8466	978	579	422	244	41			39	75	
2210 Joe	10361	987	515	368	198	31			38	73	
2290 Catherine	7479	807	467	331	172	27			38	74	
2252 Donna	7584	1013	611	454	262	41			38	74	
Foyer Front Door	7495	1266	880	729	503	128			40	72	
2212 Hellen	8405	1374	838	603	325	37			39	74	
2226 Regina	7598	1014	568	401	194	21			37	75	
2209 Karen	8758	866	470	321	155	14			35	73	
South Wall	8323	824	442	298	158	18			33	78	

These results are indicated of the locations sampled & the time the sample was taken ONLY.
Conditions & concentrations change constantly.

*Counts are sixty seconds and register a volume of 2.83 Liters of air

Chart and Graph the Particle Distribution of rooms at the test site

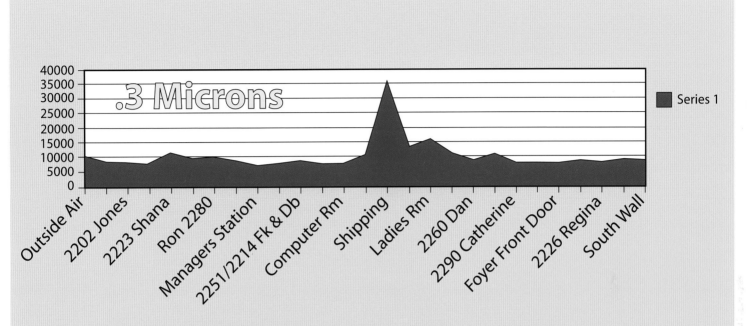

.3 Microns

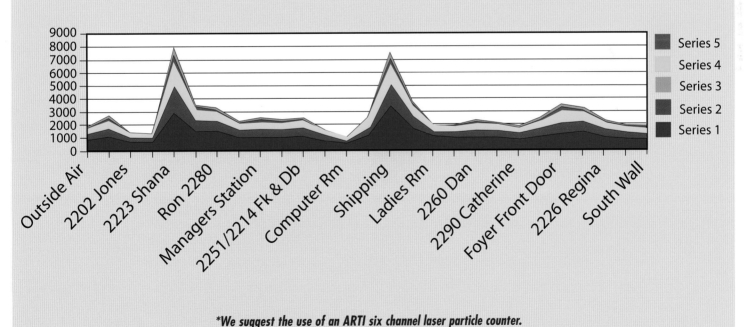

We suggest the use of an ARTI six channel laser particle counter.

The use of properly calibrated and functional equipment is imperative for assessing indoor air quality problems. Some microtesters include information regarding their testing equipment, calibrations, etc., in their final reports as substantiation of their findings.

Molds that are common to residential dwellings and drywall[1]

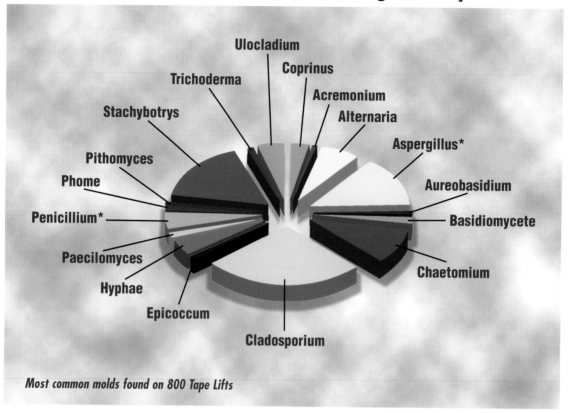

Ulocladium
Coprinus
Trichoderma
Acremonium
Stachybotrys
Alternaria
Pithomyces
Aspergillus*
Phome
Aureobasidium
Penicillium*
Basidiomycete
Paecilomyces
Chaetomium
Hyphae
Epicoccum
Cladosporium

Most common molds found on 800 Tape Lifts

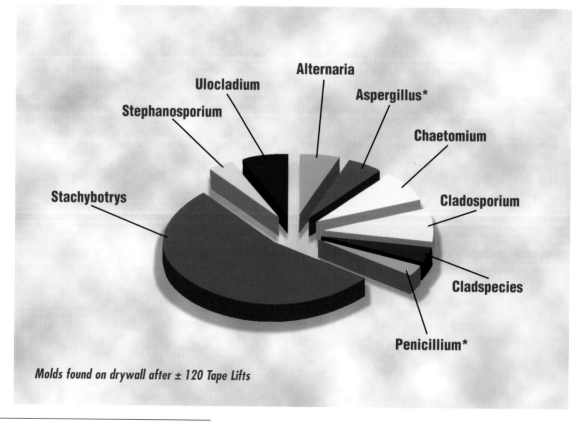

Alternaria
Ulocladium
Aspergillus*
Stephanosporium
Chaetomium
Stachybotrys
Cladosporium
Cladspecies
Penicillium*

Molds found on drywall after ± 120 Tape Lifts

[1] John Haines, 2001 annual meeting presentation, Raleigh, NC

MOLD ABATEMENT

A Brief History

Moses writes in Leviticus "*a house desecrated by mildew, mold, or fungus would be a defiled place to live in, so drastic measures had to be taken*". Moses later writes, "*On the seventh day the priest should return to inspect the house. If the mildew has spread on the walls, he is to order the contaminated stones be torn out and thrown into an unclean place outside the town. If the mildew re-appears in the house after the stones have been torn out and the house is scraped and plastered, it is a destructive mildew and the house is unclean. It must be torn down – its stones timbers and all the plaster and taken out of town.*" This was the first mold remediation and abatement plan. Moses' plan is still applicable today. We remove the mold, bag the mold, put the mold into dumpsters, and take the mold out of town.

- Later, around 1250 to 1750 Fusarium mold and Claviceps mold infected rye kernels producing toxins that resulted in miscarriages, mental disturbances, hallucination, and seizures. This was the exact time when Europe was gripped by witchcraft, demonic possessions and some wild looking art.

- In the 1920's and 1930's we had the light bulb and radio. People stayed indoors for longer periods. The depression and unemployment keep people indoors as well. Galvanized indoor plumbing was a great hit and water flowing from a spigot became a potential for water leakage.

- In the 1940's veterans returned home and baby-boomer mass-produced ranch style homes. These homes were small and build very fast. Many of the foundations were built with only eight-inch foundation block. Many of these homes were built with slabs, crawls spaces to save money, flat roofs, and under slab heating systems.

- The 1950's and 1960's homes were built with combined central heating and cooling systems. The homes had closed windows and less air exchanges. Many of these homes were built with slabs crawls and eight-inch block foundation walls.

- The 1970's was the energy crisis. Homes were built tighter and insulation use was widespread. This was the period that cer-tain asbestos products were added into insulation and put into attics. Attics were insulated to hold heat and venting was not a primary concern. Somebody also mass produced furnace humidifiers and hired very good salesmen. The invention of the split-level was common and living rooms were built several feet into the ground relying on water proofing protection.

- In the 1990's we stopped using chimneys and installed high efficient vent driven furnaces and hot water heaters. We built even tighter homes and wrapped them tight in plastic. We built with synthetic siding products, out-gassing composite timber products and indoor Jacuzzi. Somebody also mass-produced gas, ventless heaters, fireplaces, and hired some very good salesmen.

- 2000's are the multi-million dollar jury awarding years. Public awareness has been influenced from the media and from "mold is gold" attorneys.

It is true; we do have more problems today than we had in prior years. The 1920's and 1930's homes have deterioration from age, old galvanized pipes leaking, lead paint is failing, old windows leaking, and old cracking or bowed foundation walls leaking, etc. The 1940's homes also have cracking and leaking foundations due to the drain tiles being old, silted or tree root infested; their flat roofs have never-ending leaking maintenance conditions, and the ductwork under their slabs are allowing for water migration. The 1950's and 1960's furnaces are being replaced with vent-driving venting systems that are depressurizing their homes that now have additions, paneling on basement walls and finished attics that had to accommodate their growing families. These homes too have old cracking foundation systems that are beginning to leak. The tight 1970's and 1980's have mold in attics and interstitial problems because or poor building science design. The 1990's have stagnant air, interstitial moisture problems, depressurization conditions, dew points caused by improper vapor barrier installation and failing synthetic products. All these problems are now surfacing and the public is more aware of them. Mold has become the new indoor concern. Mold abatement and remediation existed during the Moses era and mold remediation is practiced now more than ever.

Exploring Remediation

- ABATEMENT is defined by *Webster's College Dictionary:* suppression or termination, noise abatement.

- REMEDIATION is defined by *Webster's College Dictionary:* fix. EPA's "Mold Remediation in Schools and Commercial Buildings": correction of something defective or deficient.

FOR THE SAKE OF THIS BOOK, WE WILL BE USING THE TERM REMEDIATION. TOTALLY ABATING A NATURALLY OCCURING CONDITION IS NEXT TO IMPOSSIBLE.

- CONTAMINANT is defined by the Institute from Inspection, Cleaning and Restoration Certification (IICRC) *S-500:* any physical, chemical, biological or radioactive substance that can have an adverse effect on air, water or soil, or any other interior or exterior surface.

- CONTAINMENT is defined by *Webster's College Dictionary:* the act or condition of containing; contain to keep under proper control.

Mold contaminants have a source. Mold contamination is best controlled at the source, as quickly as possible. This is why it is important to clean up and dry up spills, leaks, overflows, and floods within the first 48 hours. Once contamination leaves it source and gets into the surrounding environment, it is more difficult to find and clean up. This is why certain widespread practices will remove more of the construction material hosts than that of the mold effected area. For instance, contaminated drywall should be cut and removed in 2-4 foot increments past the mold infected areas. Mold remediation or abatement includes the physical removal of all growth and dispersed spores. The goal is to reduce the inside mold levels to less than that of the exterior levels.

Existing Guidelines

The following are the most common guidelines for mold remediation to date. At this time many states, universities, professional organizations are developing new guildelines. The standard of care continues to become more and more aggressive. Remediation and abatement contractors should keep up with the research and should practice the most stringent guildelines.

- EPA: "Mold Remediation in Schools & Commercial Buildings"
- NYCDOH-New York City Department of Health: "Guildelines on the Assessment and Remediation of Fungi in Indoor Environments"
- EPA: "Should You Have the Air Ducts in Your Home Cleaned"
- Summary of OSHA 1910.134: Respiratory Protection Standard
- Summary of OSHA 1910.1200: Hazard Communication Standard
- ACGIH: "Bioaerosols Assessment and Control"
- IICRC S-500: "Standard and Reference Guide for Professional Water Damage Restoration"
- EPA: "Building Air Quality-A Guide for Building Owners and Facility Managers"

The above guidelines are not the rules, but have become the standard of care until new published data becomes available. Once this data becomes available, it too should become the standard of care. Many consultants and professionals disagree with some of these guidelines and they have started to develop their own standards. Ultimately, remediation or abatement contractors are judged by how effective they are at the remediation, or remediation assignments, and if they keep the mold from re-occurring. They must also protect the workers and building occupants in this process.

The First Step

You must assess the size of the mold or moisture problem before planning remediation. The most important part of the remediation plan is to fix the water problem source. This condition must be corrected prior to any remediation or abatement. The following are questions to consider before remediation.

- Do moisture problems exist in the building?
- Have the building materials or building contents been wet for more than forty-eight hours?
- Are there any hidden sources of moisture or humidity?
- Is there moldy or musty odors? (Remember, if you see or smell mold, you have mold.)
- Are building occupants complaining about health issues?
- Do you see mold?
- How long have mold conditions existed?
- Has the building been changed or altered?

The first step is to fix the water or moisture condition. This can be done prior to or during the remediation phase. The highest priority of any plan is to protect the health and safety of the building occupants and remediators. Appropriate personal protective equipment (PPE) must be included, along within proper communication with all relevant parties. It is possible that temporary relocation of occupants will be needed. After this step is completed, the remediation phase could begin.

Key Elements In A Remediation Plan

These guidelines are for damage caused by clean water. If you know or suspect the water source is contaminated with sewage, or chemical or biological pollutants, then OSHA requires PPE and containment. An experienced professional should be contacted.

Below are strategies to respond to water damage that occurred within the first 24-48 hours.

The general concept here is to remove the moisture condition before fungal reservoirs develop. The following information can be found in full detail in the "Mold Remediation in Schools and Commercial buildings" from the U.S. EPA at *www.epa.gov/iaq/mold/graphics/moldremediation.pdf*. For more information visit our web sites at *www.REAINC.US, www.Forensicinspections.com*

WATER DAMAGED MATERIALS Recommended guidelines for response to clean water damage within 24-48 hours to prevent mold growth.

Books and papers – For non-valuable items, discard books and papers. Photocopy valuable and important items and discard the originals. Freeze in frost-free freezer or meat locker or freeze dry.

Carpet and backing – Remove water with water extraction vacuum. Reduce ambient humidity levels with dehumidifier. Accelerate drying process with fans.

Ceiling tiles – Discard and replace.

Cellulose insulation – Discard and replace.

Concrete or cinder block surfaces – Remove water with extraction vacuum. Accelerate drying process with dehumidifier, fans, and or heaters.

Fiberglass – Discard and replace.

Hard surface, porous flooring – Vacuum or damp wipe with water and mild detergent and allow to dry. Scrub if necessary.

Upholstered furniture – Remove water with water extraction vacuum. Accelerate drying process with dehumidifier, fans, and or heaters. It may be difficult to completely dry within 48 hours. If the piece is valuable, you may wish to consult with a restoration water damage professional that specializes in furniture.

Wallboard, drywall or gypsum - May be dried in place if there is no obvious swelling and the seams are intact. If not, remove, discard, and replace. Ventilate the wall cavity if possible.

Window drapes – Follow laundering or cleaning instructions recommended by the manufacturer.

Wood surfaces – Remove moisture immediately and use dehumidifier, genital heat, and fans for drying. Use caution when applying heat to hardwood floors. Treated or finished wood may be cleaned with a mild detergent and clean water, and allowed to dry. Wet paneling should be pried away from the wall for drying.

Below are strategies to respond to building materials that have, or are likely to have mold reservoirs.

The general concept here is to remove the moisture condition before fungal reservoirs develop. The following information can be found in full detail in the "Mold Remediation in Schools and Commercial buildings" from the U.S. EPA at *www.epa.gov/iaq/mold/graphics/moldremediation.pdf*. These methods were developed from literature and remediation documents including "Bioaerosols: Assessment and Control" (American Conference of Governmental Industrial Hygienists, 1999) and "IICRC S500 Standard and Reference Guild for Professional Water Damage Restoration" (Institute of Inspection, Cleaning & Restoration, 1999)

WATER DAMAGED MATERIALS Recommended guidelines for remediation of building materials with mold growth caused by clean water.

SMALL *Total surface area affected less than 10 square feet*

Material or Furnishing that is affected	Clean-up methods
Books and papers	3
Carpet and backing	1,3
Concrete or cinder block	1,3
Hard surface, porous flooring *(Linoleum, ceramic tile, vinyl)*	1,2,3
Non-porous, hard surfaces *(Plastic, metal)*	1,2,3
Upholstered furniture and drapes	1, 3
Wallboard, drywall or gypsum	3
Wood Surfaces	1, 2, 3

*Personal protection equipment is considered minimum with N-95 respirator, gloves and goggles. No containment is required.

MEDIUM *Total surface area affected between 10 and 100 square feet*

Material or Furnishing that is affected	Clean-up methods
Books and papers	3
Carpet and backing	1,3,4
Concrete or cinder block	1,3
Hard surface, porous flooring *(Linoleum, ceramic tile, vinyl)*	1,2,3
Non-porous, hard surfaces *(Plastic, metal)*	1,2,3
Upholstered furniture and drapes	1,3,4
Wallboard, drywall or gypsum	3,4
Wood Surfaces	1,2,3

*Personal protection equipment is considered limited or full. Use professional judgment; consider potential for remediator/occupant exposure, and size of contaminated area. Containment is limited.

LARGE *Total surface area affected greater than 100 square feet or potential for increased occupant or remediator exposure during remediation estimated to be significant*

Material or Furnishing that is affected	Clean-up methods
Books and papers	3
Carpet and backing	1,3,4
Concrete or cinder block	1,3
Hard surface, porous flooring (Linoleum, ceramic tile, vinyl)	1,2,3,4
Non-porous, hard surfaces (Plastic, metal)	1,2,3
Upholstered furniture and drapes	1,3,4
Wallboard, drywall or gypsum	3,4
Wood surfaces	1,2,3,4

*Personal protection equipment is considered full. Use professional judgment; consider potential for remediator/occupant exposure, and size of contaminated area. Containment is full.

Cleanup Methods

Method 1: WET VACUUM (In the case of porous material, some mold spores and fragments will remain in the material but will not grow if the material is completely dried.) Steam cleaning may be an alternative for carpets and some upholstered furniture.

Wet vacuums are vacuum cleaners designed to collect water. They could be used to remove water from floors; carpets, hard surfaces and other locations where water has accumulated. They should not be used to vacuum porous materials, such as drywall or gypsum board. They should only be used when materials are still wet, due to wet vacuum potentially spreading mold spores if not sufficiently wet or moist. At both inspections, the home was rather dry. The roof still has problems and areas still have the potential to get wet. When work is complete, the tanks, hoses, and attachments of these units should be thoroughly cleaned and dried after use, since the mold and mold spores may stick to the surfaces.

Method 2: DAMP WIPE surfaces with plain water or detergent solution (except wood; use wood floor cleaner): scrub as needed.

Whether alive or dead, mold is allergenic and may be toxic. Mold could generally be removed from non-porous (HARD) surfaces by wiping or scrubbing with water and detergent. It is important to dry these surfaces quickly and thoroughly to discourage further mold growth. Instructions for cleaning surfaces as listed on product labels should be read and followed. Porous materials that are wet and have mold growing on them should be thrown out. Molds will infiltrate substances and grow on or fill in empty spaces or crevices and may be difficult or impossible to remove completely.

Method 3: HIGH-EFFICIENCY PARTICULATE AIR VACUUM after the material that has been thoroughly dried. Dispose of the contents of the HEPA vacuum in well-sealed 6 mil plastic bags.

HEPA High Efficiency Particulate Air vacuums are necessary for areas after materials have been completely dried and contaminated materials removed. HEPA vacuums are also needed for cleanup of dust that may have settled on surfaces outside the remediation area. Care must be taken to assure that the filter is properly seated in the vacuum so that all air must pass through the filter. When changing the vacuum filter, the remediator should wear PPE to prevent exposure to the mold that has been captured. The filter and contents of the HEPA vacuum must be disposed and put in double six-mil polyethylene plastic bags.

Method 4: DISCARD – remove water-damaged materials and seal in plastic bags while inside of containment. Dispose of as normal waste, HEPA vacuum after it is dried.

PPE Personal Protective Equipment

- **Minimum:** Gloves, N-95 respirator, goggles & eye protection.
- **Limited:** Gloves, N-95 respirator or half face respirator with HEPA filter, disposable overalls, goggles and eye portion.
- **Full:** Gloves, disposable full body clothing, headgear, foot covering, full faced respirator with HEPA filter.

Containment

- **Limited:** Use polyethylene sheeting, ceiling to floor, around the affected area with a slit entry and covering flap: maintain air under negative pressure with HEPA filtered fan unit. Block supply and return air vents within containment area.
- **Full:** Use two layers of fire-retardant polyethylene sheeting with one airlock chamber. Maintain area under negative pressure with HEPA filtered fan exhausted outside of building. Block supply and return air vents within contained area.

The above criteria are conditions that only include mold reservoirs. In the real world, other contaminants will also exist. Lead paint was widely used in homes prior to 1978. Asbestos was widely used in homes prior to 1960. When water damage occurs in older homes, lead and asbestos contamination can result. In the following pages of this chapter, we will provide you with an example of how to clean up mold contamination. We will also assume that this contamination has lead and asbestos contaminants. These remediation reports are called *THE SCOPE OF WORK*.

SCOPE OF WORK

The Basics

This is an example of a scope of work developed to be the rules for the remediation processes. This scope of work is a specific detailed and well-defined systematic procedure for the mitigation specialist to follow. A scope of work could be fifty plus pages. This is an actual scope of work with some added comments (on white fields) to help better understand the process. We have broken down this scope of work into three separate sections.

image 11.1

Section One

This section is not as detailed as the *THE SCOPE OF WORK* section two. Both section one and two are significant to the remediation project. We are also assuming that the water source and leaks have been stopped and corrected.

THE EVENT
- A plumbing leak created a positive habitat for the microbial contamination in the entire building.
- The leak lasted a long time and proper drying methods were not conducted. (Recommend reading the "Restorative Drying" the complete guide to water damage restoration by Claude Blackburn DRI-EAZ Products, Inc. 11-1-98)
- This basement area has been wet from this leak for two years.
- The chimney structure also had an on-going flashing leak that was not properly fixed.
- This home was located in the State of Ohio. Every state has certain laws and the scopes of work could vary from state to state. This is significant due to the lead, asbestos and fungicide regulations.
- Prior pre-abatement testing showed severe contamination of visual mold and aerosolized mold.

These reports should always be added to the scope of work report. For this example, we will simply assume that the entire home including the attic is contaminated with visual or high concentrations of air-borne mold.

- Mold reservoirs are seen in the basement, kitchen, and other rooms.
- This is a three unit building built in 1959. Due to the home being built pre-1978, we are assuming that lead paint and asbestos conditions exists.

These test reports are not included in this example. The investigator should be careful not to forget about lead paint or asbestos issues. Remediation workers could become exposed to these contaminants if omitted.

- Prior to any work, full containment, critical barriers should be placed over all openings, exterior doors, and windows. Critical barriers should consist of six-mil polyethylene sheeting. A three-stage decontamination unit should be installed where the contractor feels it will best serve his needs. The consultant should review the location of this unit.

*There are two types of containment: full and limited. **Full containment** is defined as contaminated surface areas greater than 100 sq-ft. **Limited containment** is defined as contaminated surface areas involving between 10-100 Sq-ft. If more information is desired it could be obtained from the "Certified Mold Remediator Student Manual," offered by IAQ Training Institute, 46 South Linden Street, Suite C, Duquesne, PA 15110.*

- AFD's (Air Filtration Devices) should be installed in all units of this three-unit building. Garage is one unit, main house is one unit, and one bedroom apartment is the third unit. Several other buildings exist on this property and are not in the scope of this project. These buildings are not to be used for storage, or even entered into, due to possible cross contamination.
- Negative pressure should be installed and measured. Air scrubbers should be installed on all levels and in all sections of home during cleaning and remediation.
- Several dehumidifiers should be used in the garage unit and set to 50% humidity. The discharge of the humidifiers should be monitored. (Accidents can augment the microbial conditions.)
- No fans are permitted that would potentially spread more mold spores. If fans are to be used, the consultant should be notified.
- The consultant, prior to cleaning and prior to work, should inspect this entire system or systems.

- Prior to cleaning the household units, we recommend a preliminary step be taken due to the exhaustive amount of chattel, household items, collections, furniture, etc. It would be advised to discard all unnecessary items or items that are no longer functional and obsolete. This would include cardboard boxes, paper, magazines, food in cardboard boxes, and any other item the owner feels is no longer functional. This will make the decontamination and storage less cumbersome. These items should be placed in double six-mil polyethylene bags. If large items could not fit into bags, then polyethylene sheeting should be used. The large items should be wrapped tightly and taped prior to being discarded.

The cleaning of the entire contents should follow "IICRC 500 Guidelines." For this example, the following chart should be followed. The numbers 1,2,3,4 are all methods that are defined on page 46. All definitions below come from these "IICRC 500 Guidelines."

Some common materials and recomended cleaning methods

Books and papers	2,3,or 4,	Full PPE
Carpeting and backing	1,3,4	Full PPE
Hard surface, porous flooring (linoleum, ceramic tile, vinyl)	1,2,3 or 4	Full PPE
Concrete or cinder block	1,3	Full PPE
Non-porous hard surfaces (plastic, metals)	1,2,3	Full PPE
Wallboard (drywall and gypsum board)	3,4	Full PPE
Wood surfaces	1,2,3,or 4	Full PPE
Contained Collections (cars, stuff, etc. in glass cabinets)	2,3,or 4,	Full PPE
Upholstered furniture and drapes	1,2,3	Full PPE
Cardboard boxes	1,2,3, 4	Full PPE

*Full PPE means full protection equipment

"Certified Mold Remediator Student Manual," offered by IAQ Training Institute, 46 South Linden Street, Suite C Duquesne, PA 15110.

image 11.2

- If books and papers were contained and collections were contained in locked or closed cabinets, skip the wet wipe phase (2).
- If the paper or books have visible mold growth, they should be discarded.
- If books and papers were not contained and collections were not contained or not locked in cabinets, wet-wipe phase (2) should not be skipped.
- If the possibility of the object being ruined exists, the owner should be notified. The contractor is ultimately responsible for any damage that occurs during the cleaning phase.
- Discard all upholstered furniture, drapes and mattresses unless the contractor at the site feels he could properly clean these units. It will be less expensive to discard rather than to properly clean these objects.

image 11.3

- The contractor should make a list of all items to be discarded and have the owner sign off. The contractor should also consider taking digital photos or video of the cleaning process.

- Building materials and furnishings that are contaminated with mold growth and are not salvageable should be double bagged using six-mil polyethylene sheeting. These materials could then be discarded as ordinary construction waste.

It is important to package mold-contaminated material in sealed bags before removal from the contaminated area to minimize the dispersion of mold spores throughout the building. Large items that have heavy mold growth should be covered with polyethylene sheeting and sealed with duct tape before they are removed from the contaminated area.

- A moving truck should be used for the temporary storage of clean household items. The moving truck should bring all clean items to a clean storage facility. The items should stay at this storage facility until the mold remediation is complete. The contractor should pick a storage facility that is free of mold and has the proper atmospheric conditions. Leaving the truck on site may allow humidity levels within the truck to cause mold and mildew. Humidity control is necessary to the cleaned stored material.

- The contractor is responsible for all household items. The contractor is responsible for the cleaning, moving, storage, and the reinstallment. It is advised that the homeowner or representative inspect the items prior to cleaning and after re-installment for any damage, the contractor may have caused. All damage is the sole responsibility of the contractor.

- Full containment is required due to the job being greater than 100 Sq. Ft. A decontamination chamber or airlock should be constructed for entry into and exit from the remediation area. The entryways to the airlock from the outside and from the airlock to the main containment area should consist of a slit entry with covering flaps on the outside surface of each slit entry. The chamber should be large enough to hold a waste container and allow a person to put on and remove PPE. All contaminated PPE, except respirators, should be placed in a sealed bag while in this chamber. Respirators should be worn until remediator is outside the decontamination chamber. PPE must be worn throughout the final stages of HEPA vacuuming and damp wiping of the contaminated area. PPE must also be worn during HEPA vacuum filter changes or cleanup of the HEPA vacuum.

- All carpeting for entire dwelling should be removed by cutting into small manageable sections, rolling and wrapping in six-mil polyethylene sheeting prior to removal from the residence for disposal. All carpet tack strips should be removed. The exposed wood floors are to be cleaned during the cleaning process. (Image 11.4)

- The center kitchen wall may have hidden mold conditions. These kitchen cabinets, should be removed, decontaminated by HEPA vacuuming and/or wet wiping with a detergent water solution, and wrapped in six-mil polyethylene sheeting prior to removal from the residence.

- The home heating system should be shut down. All openings, all registers, and all returns should be sealed with double six-mil plastic. These locations should be double taped. After all work is completed, the entire system should be decontaminated and cleaned professionally. Cleaning of ductwork should be done by certified personnel and follow all stated guidelines.

For more information, please refer to the "ACR 2002 Assessment Cleaning & Restoration of HVAC Systems," an industry standard developed by the National Air Duct Cleaners Association NADCA 1518K Street, N.W. , Suite 503 Washington, DC 20005.

- All tile, linoleum, and mastic should be reviewed at the demolition phase. The contractor should notify the consultant of this condition if found. If asbestos material is present, proper asbestos removal techniques should be implemented. The consultant could perform an asbestos risk assessment if insurance carrier or owner is willing to pay additional fees. Asbestos containing materials must be handled only be certified workers. Asbestos containing materials must be disposed of at the proper dump site.

image 11.4

- The drywall should be removed by cutting into small manageable sections rolling and double wrapping in six-mil polyethylene sheeting prior to removal from the residence for disposal. Drywall removal should be done to the following locations that had visual mold reservoirs. The kitchen ceiling, the kitchen center wall, the living room ceiling, the living room center wall, the bathroom ceiling, the bathroom center wall, the bedroom adjacent to the bathroom ceiling, the bedroom adjacent to the bathroom center wall. (All walls /ceilings that were adjacent to the chimney structure.)

- All the attic insulation should be removed. This location will be highly contaminated and proper PPE is needed. After all insulation and all other debris are removed, the entire area should be HEPA vacuumed. The insulation should be double bagged in six-mil plastic bags. Proper cleaning methods still need to be applied as stated in previous sections.

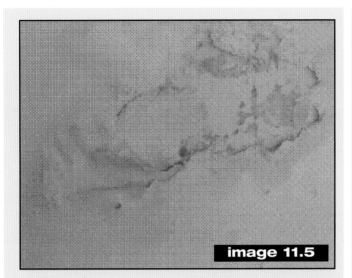

image 11.5

image 11.6

- All exposed joists, rafters, studs and plywood decking should be decontaminated. It should be decontaminated by using a detergent and water solution and a wire brush. Do not soak. The wood should be scrubbed with the wire brush or equivalent until all visible molds are gone. After wire brushing, the timbers should be washed with a water detergent solution. After washing, towel drying should be done. The final step will require a fine mist of water and bleach solution. Do not soak. This solution should only be in surface contact for no more than 10 minutes. The water and bleach solution should be 10 parts water to one part bleach. Antimicrobial solutions or other products could be used and should be applied according to manufacturer directions. During the washing, scrubbing phase, the contractor should use additional commercial grade dehumidifiers to lower humidity levels.

- This treatment should be done to all basement joists, all exposed studs after drywall demolition, and attic rafters. After all cleaning is complete; all cleaned wood should be sprayed with a sealer paint that also has a mold inhibitor product.

- All other surface in the entire dwelling should be properly cleaned. All walls and ceilings will require new paint.

See page 48 for sample material processing information.

- Workers are permitted only in designated worker areas.

- Humidity should be controlled for the entire project. Levels of 50 % or lower should be target levels.

- The contractor is responsible for fees encountered by post abatement testing. Failures will require retesting at additional fees.

Refer to Section five for testing protocols.

- Containment must remain sealed and under negative pressure until all viable post abatement testing has passed. Generally, this process takes 14-18 days. During this entire phase, the home occupants will have to find living quarters. The occupants will not be able to move back until the post abatement testing is complete. An additional three to four weeks may pass after remediation is complete. The occupant should consider two to three months.

- New construction is not part of this scope. New drywall, new carpet and pad, new insulation, new roof, new flashing, new furniture, new paint, new window treatments, and many other installations need to be bid on by remodeling contractors. The consultant will not monitor this phase of the project. It is advised that an architect or construction manager be employed.

SCOPE OF WORK

Section Two

Section two is more complex, with much more detail pertaining to this remediation process. Section two has more rules, guidelines, laws, and regulations that the contractors doing work should know. When working with insurance companies, this type of report is common practice. This particular scope of work is one that is used in Eastern States.

The following pages are an example of what contractors should follow when performing remediation. This is only one sample and many different variations of this sample could be made. This sample is one that was put together from the Ohio laws, EPA protocols, and other sample scopes of work from other environmental consulting firms. This sample also assumes that this project has lead paint and asbestos hazards. Lead and asbestos reports are not listed in this book. This sample is rather stringent, and smaller jobs may require a smaller scope of work.

APPLICABLE REGULATIONS FOR MICROBIAL REMEDIATION

Below are only some regulations that could apply to the microbial remediation, restoration, abatement, or removal of this sample project. When lead paint or asbestos are being removed additional regulations will apply.

- OSHA General Industry Standard 29CFR 1910.
- OSHA Respiratory Protection Standard, 29 CFR Parts 1910.134 and 1926 Subpart M Fall protection(Contractor could download these OSHA requirements from internet sources)
- Federal, State and Local Administrative Statues, Codes and Rules may be applicable. (Contractor should be cognizant and is ultimately responsible in knowledge of these potential applicable requirements).
- When applicable, Permit Required Confined Space Entry Program (29 CRF 1910.146).
- Contractor should provide appropriate permits for demolition, electrical, HVAC, plumbing and general construction as required by local municipalities.
- Any other new developed guideline from significant authority. Due diligence and standard of care should be practiced.

The General Contractor and all Sub-Contractors are responsible for knowing, determining, and ultimately complying with the above-mentioned applicable regulations. Most of the above could be downloaded from the internet.

SOME MINIMAL REQUIREMENTS FOR BIDDING CONTRACTORS

Bidding contractors should have one or more of the following credentials or experience for this example project. The contractor should be licensed in the city of Cleveland Ohio to perform work.

- State licensed to perform asbestos removal. These individual are already trained in containment type protocols.
- State licensed to perform lead paint, lead dust or lead soil removal. These individuals are already trained in containment type protocols.
- Registered General Contractors in fire restoration business.
- Dewatering contractors.
- Contractors that performed mold remediation projects in the last two years.
- Professional Engineer or Architect.
- Engineer with certifications in pollution type contaminants.
- Government official performing duties in pollutions control.
- Licensed General Pest Applicator with experience in fungicide.
- CIE, CMRS, CMR, IH, CIH, CAIH, CIAQT, CIAQM, CIAQI, CIAQI, CMC, CMI, CMRS, CMCA, CSP, or equivalent could perform work as long as they have documented and completed a minimum of three similar projects.

TEMPORARY UTILITY / STORAGE / EQUIPMENT / WORK HOURS

Temporary Lighting and Power

Power being used should not originate in the containment areas. This power should be taken from the electrical service outside the containment work area. Only licensed electricians complying with the NEC® National Electrical Code, OSHA Occupational Safety and Health Administration regulations, UL Underwriters Laboratories and other relevant state or local codes, should do all electrical taps, installations, and configurations.

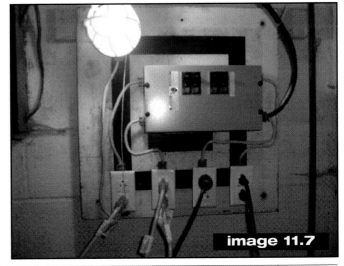
image 11.7

image 11.8

All Circuits should be GFCI'S Ground Fault Circuit Interrupter type. Image 11.7 is an example what a temporary GFCI circuit board could look like. This board was designed for this particular project. Large equipment machines such as air-scrubbers, negative air machines, large fans, high volume dehumidifiers or other equipment, that use more than 10 amps, should be on it is own circuit. The electrician should calculate the number of amps used per circuits, especially if equipment is running during non-work hours. Certain projects may require a night watchman to make sure all equipment is operating.

Temporary lighting should consist of stand-alone fixtures that are all connected to GFCI circuits. Several light fixtures may be used for the same circuit as long as the electrician performs the calculations necessary for amperage use. Make sure the watts used are high enough to see all mold conditions.

Lighting candlepower should be adequate as noted by OSHA or other requirements established by governing authorities.

Temporary Water

All temporary water connections should be connected to back flow preventions. All street hydrant water usage should be in accordance with city guidelines and permits needed when applicable. A water meter should be installed if using city water hydrant water. All discharge of gray water should be disposed of properly. If debris is mixed with the gray water, it should be cleaned or screened and discarded properly. All discharge terminations should be designed as not to allow cross contamination.

Storage locations

All operations of the contractor should be confined to areas authorized or pre-approved by the owner, project manager, consultant, or other significant authority.

image 11.9

Scaffolding and Ladders

Rolling scaffolding and/or power lifts should be made available for use by the environmental consultant during post remediation inspections and testing. Contractor should be aware that post-remediation inspections may be several days or weeks after the project completion. All scaffolding and ladders should meet OSHA standards and comply with local building codes. The contractor should put in his or her bid the fee for this equipment rental, equipment installation and equipment removal.

Project Schedules and Working Hours

The contractor should be available to work with appropriate and consistent sized crews continuously from the beginning to the end of the project. The number of days and hours that work is permitted should be provided to the contractor prior to bidding. As this property is located in Cleveland Ohio, the contractor should check city ordinances for start, end, and weekend work hours. The contractor must finish the project according to the deadline date that is indicated on the bid project. The contractor could be fined $500 daily, for each additional date after the deadline. All fines and regulations are different from project to project and contract to contract.

SUBMITTALS FOR MICROBIAL REMEDIATION

Listed below are items that should be made available upon request prior to beginning of work. Furthermore, the listed items should be submitted to the consultant in charge of the job.

- Supervisor of the project should submit his or her qualifications. (People with Supervisor standings in Asbestos or Lead Paint, Hazardous Materials handling, Engineers, Architects, CIE, CMRS, CMR, CIH, CAIH, CIAQT, CIAQM, CIAQI, CIAQI, CMC, CMI, CMRS, CMCA, CSP, IH, or similar education, certifications, license, or experience qualifications should submit these papers.)

- Sub-contractor's workers and HVAC people should submit their qualifications. Under no circumstance should HVAC personnel enter or work on the project that are not familiar or trained with pollution type abatements.(Certifications from such organizations such as the NADCA National Air Duct Cleaners Association, is an acceptable organization. For information, contact them at 202-737-2926 or 202-347-8847, or at nadca@aol.com.)

- Daily reports or logs should be submitted and kept in duplicate. Daily reports and/or logs should contain all necessary information: date, time, weather, interior temperature, exterior temperature, humidity interior, humidity exterior, men on site, equipment used, quality control data, work done, items brought to site, items removed from site, site meeting, safety meeting, quality control meetings, problems encountered, site visitors, PPE used, date for negative air, times of filter changes, and all other necessary information. A safety program for this project needs to be submitted. This safety program should include emergency exits, fire protection equipment, site location of the first aid kit, security measures to protect the public, security measures to protect the jobsite. The project should, at all times, have access to a phone or cellular phone for emergency calls.

- All chemical LABELS and MSDS's should be submitted. All chemicals, LABELS and MSD's should be posted at the job site for all to see and read. All bottles and like containers should be properly labeled according to standards and regulations. Under no circumstance should the contractor apply spray or fog, using chemicals that do not have MSDS sheets or approved submittals.

- In many states, a contractor needs to be licensed to apply chemicals that are considered pesticides. A pesticide is defined as any product intended for preventing, destroying, repelling, or mitigating any pest or a plant growth regulator, defoliant, or desiccant. Therefore, products such as insecticides, herbicides, rodenticides, and fungicides are all considered "pesticides". Contractors applying pesticides should be familiar with Ohio Administrative Code, Ohio Pest Law, and FIFRA Federal Insecticide, Fungicide, and Rodenticide Act. (Ohio Department of Agriculture Pesticide Regulation Section at 614-728-6987 or 1-800-282-1955.) NOTE: These are stringent requirements and it is recommended that if a contractor does not have these qualifications, he or she should use products that are not covered under these laws or employ sub-contractors that have these credentials. If the contractor is to apply pesticides, a copy of his license should be submitted.

- The disposal of pollution or contaminated materials should be done in accordance to acceptable methods: Equipment used, transportation vehicles, location of certified dumping grounds etc. Proper records should be kept according to USEPA and State Laws governing disposals. Job site records should be kept concerning all material removed from sites.

- A copy of the respiratory protection program along with personal protective equipment that will be used, should be submitted. Submittals should include the type of respirators that will be used and the type of PPE needed for a certain contamination concentration.

The contractor should consider utilizing the following related items pertaining to the employee-training program. (All contractors should have an employee-training program on file.)

image 11.10

- Protective clothing.

- Protective equipment.

- Protective rules for working environment.

- Respirator fit tests for all workers and supervisors or other personnel that would be entering the project site.

- Emergency fire procedures that include egress

- Emergency exits due to equipment failure.

- Emergency exits due to PPE failure.

- Emergency conditions due to weather, leaks, spillage, or other potential conditions that could occur. Prior to all jobs, the contractor should make a list of all potential emergencies that could occur and have an action plan.

- Location of job phone with all necessary phone numbers.

- Location of the clean area for changing, showering, and preparing for the job site entry and exits. Some jobs will not require showering facilities.

- Procedure for entering clean into the job site and leaving dirty from the job site.

The above could be submitted in a narrative format as long as all areas are covered. If certain submittals require certifications, licenses or continued education requirements, the contractor or sub-contractor should make these items available upon request.

WORKER AND JOBSITE EXPOSURES

It is important that workers, supervisors, inspectors, owners, project managers, construction managers and all personnel that enter the project be properly trained and understand the potential risks. The exposures, to or contact with, large concentrations of bio-growth presents a potential health risk to all people involved in the removal process and all people who enter the project during remediation. Risks may include hypersensitivity, pneumonitis, allergic respiratory disease, asthma etc. Personnel with pre-existing chronic disease or are immune compromised or sensitized are at greater risk. If asbestos is present, then other rules apply, such as initial chest x-rays prior to job start or other requirements specified by the consultant or owner.

RECORD KEEPING FOR PROJECT

The job site should have an operational job file. This job file should have all job records, licenses, insurance papers, etc. This file should be out of the immediate work or contamination zone. This file should be made available to all parties that have authority to view it.

- The job site should have a **Daily Project Log**. The following but not limited to, should be included in this daily log:

- Date, weather, outside humidity, outside temperature, interior project humidity, interior project temperature and any other weather related condition. (The contractor could purchase a hydrometer for roughly $75.00 from a third party supply house or they could call Professional Equipment at 1-800-334-9291.)

- Work scope performed, men on site working, PPE used, respirator filter changes, equipment used, equipment maintenance, problems occurred on site, phone calls made to off site offices that pertain to this project, materials delivered to site, materials removed from site, failures, accidents and any other relevant condition.

- The job site should have a **Visitor's Log**. All visitors should sign in to this logbook when arriving and leaving the project. Furthermore, the visitors should indicate on this log their reason for visit. Under no circumstance should visitors enter into the contamination zone without proper PPE. All rules should apply to all visitors.

- The job site should have a binder that contains all other reports. These reports are, and not limited to inspections, tests, city inspections, certifications, licenses, dump record, complaints, and any other relevant job report.

ALL ITEMS ABOVE SHOULD BE NEAT, IN ORDER AND LOCATED IN ONE CENTRAL LOCATION. THESE RECORDS ARE TO BE MADE AVAILABLE TO ALL AUTHORIZED PERSONNEL.

PERSONAL PROTECTION

A Personal protection plan is necessary for all jobs. For smaller jobs and jobs that are not lead paint, or asbestos related the personal protection plan could be made smaller.

- Respiratory Protection: The contractor should provide all workers with personally issued and marked respiratory protection equipment approved by NIIOSH or similar. All respirators should be fit tested and not interchanged with different workers. Respirators that are not fit tested are not permitted on job. (Most cities have certified companies that could perform fit testing.)

- Project set up: Workers should wear full-face respirator equipped with P-100 filter cartridges or equal. (Half face respirators could be substituted for smaller jobs or when applicable.)

- Application of Chlorine compounds: All workers involved in applying chlorine-based biocides or cleaning solutions should wear full-face respirators with P-100 pre-filter cartridges and cartridges approved for use of chlorine or acid gas or equal. (All chemicals will have a MSDS sheet that will also advise on respirator type.)

- Other: When there is a possibility of exposure to microbial volatile organic compounds, acid, other fumes and mold spores, a combination cartridge addressing these items should be employed. The appropriate cartridges are purple and yellow. NIIOSH literature could provide all information pertaining to respirators and color codes.

- Protective clothing, hats, gloves etc: The contractor should provide protective disposable clothing. The clothing should be full body with coveralls, head caps, and boots. The three should be one piece and all watertight. The contractor should provide hard hats if required by other job conditions. Other protective items other than disposable clothing (Tyvek™/ Saranex™) should be decontaminated if re-used. If tears occur in the coveralls, the worker is to remove, shower, and change into a new coverall suit. Contractor is to provide various size coverall suits to fit needs of workers. Workers should wear one size larger due to comfort levels. It is very common for workers to change clothing three to six times daily. The contractor should have plenty of disposable suits on the project.

- Signs: The contractor should provide warning signs that are to be posted at all entrances or openings to the enclosed work area. Signs should state, "WARNING: DO NOT ENTER– Microbial Remediation in Progress". Signs could be altered as long as approved by the consultant.

EMERGENCY PROCEDURES

- Emergency procedures should be developed prior to job start. Appropriate signs should be posted. Signs should be posted for all individuals to see prior to entering the job site. All working personnel and other job visitors should acknowledge and understand the site conditions, potential health affects, exits, and other emergency procedures. When applicable, the contractor should implement for the handicapped.

- When wet conditions allow for slippery surfaces, the contractor should implement a plan to control such conditions. Six-mil plastic floor sheathing generally will be slippery.

- When demolition of walls, floors, and ceilings is being done, all power should be shut off. As mentioned earlier, the contractor should provide a site sub panel with all GFCI'S outlets for all site lights and equipment.

- The contractor should take consideration of fire, explosion, toxic conditions, electrical hazards and confined spaces.

- The contractor should provide portable fire extinguishers within the contamination areas. The contractor should also provide fire extinguishers outside the contamination area. Consult with the NFPA N10-1984 for detailed information on type of fire extinguisher needed.

IF BIOLOGICAL OR CHEMICAL CONDITIONS EXIST, CONTRACTOR SHOULD ALLOCATE SECURITY FOR UNAUTHORIZED PERSONNEL OR POTENTIAL TERRORIST.

PREPARATION OF WORK AREA

Many of the below conditions would not apply for smaller jobs or jobs that do not have lead or asbestos hazards. Many of the variables could change also depending on type of work. In all scopes of work, discrepancy may arise and when they do, the more stringent method should apply.

- Household Items: All household items including furnishings, moveable objects should be moved by the contractor to a secure and clean area as designated by the owner. These household items should be cleaned of all contaminants prior to storage. The cleaning should be done by previously indicated methods. Certain household items could not be properly washed and will need to be discarded. All discarded items are to be double bagged and thrown out. The flow chart in the earlier section should be followed.

- HVAC and Electrical Systems: Prior to construction barrier and containment enclosure installation, the contractor should shut down all HVAC and electrical components. All returns and registers should be taped and shut down. It is advised that after project completion all ductwork and HVAC systems be cleaned and purged of contamination. (For more information, read all sections in the ACR 2002 "Assessment Cleaning & Restoration of HVAC System" by NADCA.)

- Critical barriers and containment enclosures: All locations that will receive temporary barriers, tape, six-mil polyethylene sheeting, contaminants should be HEPA vacuumed and damp-wiped with a bleach solution. All openings such as, vents, plenums, corridors, returns, exhaust air ducts, diffusers, doorways, electrical outlets, switches, and windows, should be covered with one layer of six-mil polyethylene sheeting held securely in place. Two layers of six-mil polyethylene sheeting should be secured to existing structures or to the temporary

image 11.11

isolation structure. Temporary isolation walls when applicable are required to form the perimeter of the containment work area. These temporary isolation walls should extend from the floor to as close as possible to the decking or ceiling above. All penetrations of ductwork, piping, and conduit that pass through walls should be covered with one layer of six-mil polyethylene sheeting. All gaps, holes, and penetrations should be sealed with one layer of six-mil polyethylene sheeting. All openings greater than twenty-four square feet should be framed with wood studs at sixteen-inch centers. The contractor could use other framing techniques as long as they are sound and stable. All walls that are not being removed should be covered with one layer of six-mil polyethylene sheeting. The floor should be covered first with the six-mil polyethylene layer extending 12 inches up the walls. The six-mil polyethylene wall layer should extend and overlap this six-inch floor layer. All joints and laps should have a minimum of a six-inch splice.

- Negative pressure system: The contractor should provide four to six air exchanges per hour in the containment area. The contractor should provide and maintain a negative air differential of 0.02 inches of water inside the work area. This pressure should be continuous and not interrupted until post abatement testing has been completed and is satisfactory.

The contractor should have necessary equipment to monitor negative air and see that proper air exchanges occur. The contractor should implement the use of AFD's air filtration devices with HEPA filters as part of the exhaust ventilation. The contractor should change all filters as recommended by the manufacturer and keep records of these changes. The contractor could implement the use of partial counters to gain greater life of filters. All particle count data should be recorded and documented. All used filters should be double bagged with six-mil polyethylene and discarded as waste. The contractor may, if he chooses, create positive air in clean areas using the filtered discharge air from the containment area. The consultant should verify this.

- The contractor should provide portable fire extinguishers within the contamination areas. The contractor should also provide fire extinguishers outside the contamination area. Consult with the NFPA N10-1984 for detailed information on type of fire extinguisher needed. All fire extinguishers should have their dated certifications attached. All fire extinguishers that have expired certification should be changed.

- Exhaust should be to the outdoors. The hole in the enclosure should be taped and properly sealed. Exhaust and filtered air could be brought back into the dwelling to create positive pressure under the consultant's direction. When doing this the contractor should check exhaust air periodically with a laser particle counter for quality control.

DECONTAMINATION UNITS

The following system is roughly the same system that asbestos and lead paint abatement contractors use. Smaller projects may not warrant the below systems.

- Decontamination unit: The unit should consist of three rooms in series, separated from each other. The walls for this decontamination unit should be constructed with a temporary isolation wall. These walls should be constructed with two layers of six-mil polyethylene sheeting. The floor of these decontamination units should be two layers of six-mil polyethylene sheeting. The doors between the rooms should be double flap overlapping polyethylene curtains. Air locks should be thirty-six inches with a triple-flap doorway that separate the rooms. All double flaps and triple flap doorways should be weighted at the bottom. The height of this decontamination unit should be a minimum of seventy-eight inches from the floor. The following three rooms are as follows:

- The clean room should be for changing into clean cloths. The clean room should contain new Tyvek suits, new respirators, new gloves, and other personal protection equipment. Tools, demolition equipment, and materials should not be stored in this room.

- The shower room should contain hot and cold water. In hot weather climates, hot water may not be necessary. Other conditions may not permit the use of hot water. The shower room should contain a drain to collect the gray water. Workers should be told to minimize use of water due to the water going generally into temporary drains. This water should be discarded appropriately according to type of contamination. The shower room should be inspected daily to ensure no leakage is occurring from the temporary plumbing system. The contractor is responsible of removing this water and not leaving on the job site. (Improper shower installation and maintenance could cause additional microbial contamination.)

- Primary decontamination room should be used for storage of equipment, tools, and other materials. A labeled drum, lined with at least six-mil polyethylene sheeting, should be provided to collect discarded protective clothing.

The contractor may rent or purchase pre-constructed decontamination units. These units could be attached to the doorway of the structure. When applicable, the contractor may the use of the house facilities in lieu of decontamination units.

INSPECTION OF DECONTAMINATION UNIT AND ALL SITE PREPARATIONS

The contractor should notify the consultant to inspect the entire site, placed equipment, decontamination unit, and all other site protocols. If changes are to be made to the scope of work, this inspection should be the appropriate time to discuss modifications, or changes with the consultant. The consultant should be given ample time to make necessary decisions. Written authorization should be provided prior to any scope of work changes.

CLEANUP

The cleaning of the entire contents should follow IICRC 500 Guidelines. For this example, this chart is in the previous Section One of the Scope of Work.

- Porous material requires removal and disposal. This would include drywall, carpeting, insulation, books, partial board, newspaper, etc. The contractor should remove these materials so large amounts of mold spores are not released. These materials should be double bagged with six-mil polyethylene sheeting. All carpet and rugs should be HEPA vacuumed prior to disposal.

- Non-porous material should be cleaned and reused. This would include metals, glass, hard plastic, etc. Other semi non-porous items such as wood, plaster, and concrete should be cleaned and reused when applicable. All cleaning should be done using detergent solutions that are safe and non toxic. The contractor should be responsible for all damaged material caused by this cleaning process. The contractor should be cognizant of morality or mixing of solutions. The contractor should also be cognizant of chemical reactions when mixing.

- All structurally connected items such as joists, beams, plates, bridging or like construction components could remain in place. They could be wire brushed, sanded, or scrubbed with abrasive scoring pad or other system.

- As mentioned earlier, air ducts and furnace should be sealed off prior to mold remediation. These units should stay sealed off until the entire remedial phase is complete. These units should be cleaned in accordance to NADCA document entitled, "General Specifications for the Cleaning of Commercial Heating Ventilation and Air Conditioning Systems" modified from residential systems. The cleaning phase should be done prior to post abatement testing. The final clean up should conducted after the air ducts and furnace are properly cleaned. Special provisions may be needed for certain duct products.

image 11.12

DOMESTIC WATER AND HUMIDITY

- The job site relative humidity should be below 55%. The consultant should monitor the humidity and advise the contractor during the project phase. The contractor should implement the use of dehumidifiers to get the humidity below 55%. The contractor might need to run several heavy-duty de-humidifiers. If the humidity is above 60% at job completion, the contractor should inform the owner that other measures are necessary to control the high humidity. A written letter is advised and should contain the following language: Levels of 50% and lower of indoor relative humidity are desirable for indoor microbial amplification. Moisture conditions and upper levels of indoor relative humidity should be lowered and controlled to ensure future home cleanliness of mold spores or mold amplification.

- A bleach, biocide, and disinfectant solution of water should be used in sparse amounts when used for dust control. It could be applied with a manual 1-gallon sprayer or a fogging machine. When applicable, if the mold to be removed is dry, the contractor should carefully wet this area to minimize dust and airborne mold spores during his or her demolition. Indoor dry surface must be defined by probe moisture meter of moisture content of less than 14%. If the contractor is to implement this method, he or she should be careful not to wet down surface that are not to be removed. All surfaces that would receive this method should be removed within one hour of getting wet.

- Surfaces that are to be cleaned should be done using damp-wiping methods. Under no circumstance should these surfaces be soaked or become saturated.

- Removal of all mixtures domestic tap water residual is necessary immediately with a HEPA vacuum or dry mop. The mop head should be replaced daily and double bagged.

POST REMEDIATION OR REMOVAL CLEANING (AFTER PASSING VISUAL INSPECTION BY THE CONSULTANT)

- All the disposable material and supplies should be double bagged and discarded. The entire work area should be HEPA vacuumed, and cleaned with a detergent solution and wiped down with a 15:1 bleach solution. The work should start from the ceiling elevation and work down to the floor elevation. The owner should be informed that all walls and ceilings might require new paint due to being discolored from cleaning solutions.

- Polyethylene Barrier Removal: Prior to removal, clean all polyethylene sheeting with a HEPA vacuum. Damp wipe all polyethylene sheeting prior to removal using bleach solution. The first layer of polyethylene should be treated in the same manor as indicated above. After this layer has been removed, four hours of time should pass or a minimum of four full air exchanges. Once completed, the second layer of polyethylene should be treated in the same manner as indicated above.

- The critical isolation barriers should remain in place. All other remaining surfaces should be cleaned using a HEPA vacuum. All surfaces should be damp wiped with detergent solution. A final bleach solution wipe down should be done on the last step.

POST ABATEMENT TEST (PAT)

All post abatement testing is to be done after a thorough visual has been completed of all areas under remediation. Under no circumstances will air testing be done if visual mold is present. If mold is encountered at other locations, it needs to be abated prior to any other additional post abatement test. There are no national protocols for PAT. Each consultant will develop his or her protocols incorporating the industry standards and due diligence.

- All post abatement tests should be done by a qualified third party being a CIE, CMRS, CMR, CIH, CAIH, CIAQT, CIAQM, CIAQI, CIAQI, CMC, CMI, CMRS, CMCA, CSP, IH, PE, Engineer, or equivalent.

- All tests should be done a minimum of forty-eight hours after remediation process has terminated or after a minimum of one hundred air exchanges. The contractor is not allowed to fog or spray sanitizer during these forty-eight hours.

These requirements could change depending on project size.

- All PAT's should be conducted with all portable air moving, cleaning, negative air devices or machines shut down.

- There should be a minimum of four tests taken, one of which should be of clean air to be used as a baseline. When budget permits, a blank test should be conducted. When budget permits, all rooms should be tested.

- There should be a PAT taken in each area that has been abated.

- Test placement should duplicate the locations of the pre-abatement tests. PAT's should be compared to the pre-abatement tests.

- The results are to be reviewed by a competent person.

- For results to be satisfactory, counts should be equal to or below the exterior test results. There should be no *Stachybotrys* or *Fusarium* in the air.

- There are no established government standards for mold contamination.

- The testing laboratory should be EMPAT certified and or should be accredited by the AIHA.

- The device used for the clearance test is to be Air- O- Cell cassettes by Zeflon Inc. or equivalent.

- The pump is to be calibrated with a rotimeter prior to testing and after every fifth test.

- The test should be conducted at a pump rate of fifteen liters per minute.

- Each test should be run for five minutes.

BARRIER REMOVAL / FINAL CLEANUP / RETURN OF HOUSEHOLD ITEMS AND UTILITIES

- The post abatement testing must be acceptable prior to any barrier removal. All surfaces behind barriers should be HEPA vacuumed. These surfaces should include and not be limited to walls, floors, ceilings, windows, and doors. The contractor should also HEPA vacuum all adjacent interior spaces and surfaces within 10 feet of the former location of barriers.

- The contractor should remove all equipment and garbage from the site once all final cleaning is complete, and there is acceptance of post abatement testing.

- When applicable and if the contract requires, the contractor should reestablish all household items from the temporary location to the original location. The contractor should not move any item back into the clean environment that is dirty or contaminated.

- All utilities and fixtures are to be activated.

DISPOSAL AND BAGGING

- A dumpster should be located on the site. This dumpster should have a protective cover. The cover is to be installed to protect the environment. The cover should be able to withstand reasonable wind snow or rain conditions. All disposable containers should be double bagged with six-mil polyethylene sheeting. Large items should be double wrapped with six-mil polyethylene sheeting and all ends taped to form a tight seal. All materials removed that are to be discarded should be removed from the site at the end of each workday. Disposal of dumpster should be done according to EPA, state, and local authorities.

Microbial waste could generally be disposed of in normal landfills. Asbestos and lead paint containing material may require special treatment and special disposal. You should check with the regulations, laws, rules that apply for the location of the remediation project. If certain chemicals are to be used during remediation, hazardous waste rules should apply.

- All chemicals, pesticides, biocides, fungicides should have proper MSDS papers and all rules on MSDS papers apply. It is advised that separate dumpsters be used under these conditions. The contractor should properly remove and dispose of asbestos when applicable.

SECTION TWELVE
Contamination Levels

GENERAL LEVES OF CONTAMINATION

An important step in the abatement of indoor mold infestation is the correct level identification of the existing problem. Each of the levels will generally require different specific remediation processes. The following graphics and descriptions should help you to differentiate between the four general levels of contamination.

1) Level I: Image 12.1
If the area of mold is 2 square feet or less.
A) Individuals who have received training on proper clean up methods, protection, and potential health hazards can clean this area. These individuals should be free from asthma, allergy, and immune disorders. Gloves and a half face respirator should be worn.
B) Contaminated material should be placed in a sealed plastic bag before taking it out of the building. This will prevent contamination of other parts of the building.
C) Surrounding areas should be cleaned with household bleach.

2) Level II: Image 12.2
If the area of mold is more than 2 square feet but less than 30 square feet, then the recommendations are the same as Level I; the added precaution is that moldy materials should be covered with plastic sheets and taped before any handling or removal is done. For instance, a moldy panel of gypsum board (measuring 4 feet by 8 feet) wall would need to have plastic sheeting taped over the affected area on the wall, before the wallboard is cut to remove the contaminated section. Once cut from the wall, that section should be placed within another layer of plastic before it is carried through the building for disposal.

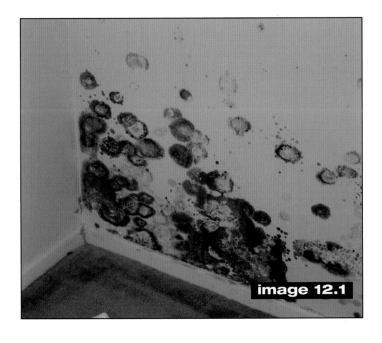
image 12.1

image 12.2

3) Level III: Image 12.3

If the area of mold is more than 30 square feet, then personnel trained in handling of hazardous materials (such as asbestos) are necessary. Specific recommendations for hazardous materials workers can be found in the New York document.

4) Level IV: Images 12.4 and 12.5

If *Stachybotrys chartum* is shown to be present in the heating, ventilation, or air conditioning system, then recommendations are the same as for Level III.

Correction of Visible Mold

Visual identification of black mold in a chronically wet area is considered to be a possible indicator of *Stachybotrys chartum* or other mold. The New York City Department of Health convened an expert panel on *Stachybotrys chartum* in May 1993, which recommended different methods of mold removal depending on the size of the mold problem. Their recommendations are summarized below.

Summary

In summary, *Stachybotrys chartum* and other molds may cause health symptoms that are nonspecific. At present there is no test that proves an association between *Stachybotrys chartum* and particular health symptoms. Individuals with persistent symptoms should see their physician. However, if *Stachybotrys chartum* or other molds are found in a building, prudent practice recommends that they be removed. The simplest and most expedient remediation that properly and safely removes mold should be used.

image 12.3

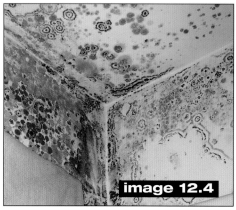

image 12.4

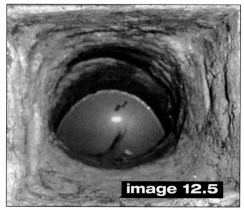

image 12.5

SECTION THIRTEEN
Forensic Investigation

FORENSICS / PSYCHROMETRICS / BUILDING SCIENCE / SITE NOTES

Site One

This condominium unit was located in a high-rise tower. The new owner of this unit recently found some microbial reservoirs. After moving in he was told by a different occupant that this condominium project had moisture conditions during the initial construction.

Site Conditions
1. Fungal reservoirs on drywall surfaces
2. Fungal reservoirs in interstitial spaces
3. Fungal reservoirs at improperly abated locations

Field Notes

The following are field data from moisture and humidity mapping. We only calculated the dew point at one of the below samples. The east bedroom wall was the coldest, therefore we plotted to determine and to view the dew point graph. (See p.62)

Location	Ambient temperature °F	RH%	Exterior wall temperature °F	Interior wall temperature °F	Floor temperature °F	Ceiling temperature °F
Living Room	68.0	36.8	66.8	70	71.2	72
Bedroom East	68.4	33.2	64	67.4	66.6	66.6
Bedroom west	68.8	31.1	na	70.2	71	70
Exterior	49.5	52.6	DEW Point 33.3 °F	na	na	na

Moisture and humidity mapping results

The entire condominium unit was mapped for room temperature, room humidity, surface temperature, and moisture content. The sling psychrometer was used for baseline testing results and the digital hygrometer was used for the data collection. All surface moisture mapping was conducted using the Delmhorst moisture-testing gauge and an infrared laser thermometer. All values are represented in mathematical terms to determine potential cause of fungal development.

The following mathematical representation depicts that during our inspection, the dew point for the above condition was 38.4°F. In conclusion, the condominium unit conditions did not have moisture levels nor did it have humidity levels that would cause dew points today. Dew points and moisture are necessary for microbial manifestation and amplification. This data can change from day to day. This data does not depict all present or past interstitial conditions. Due to this conclusion and other field observations, three core cuts were conducted to observe the interstitial cavity space.

Core cuts one and two were performed to an interior partition wall. Core cut three was conducted to an exterior wall.

image 13.1

Bedroom east exterior wall

PSYCHROMETRIC CHART
Normal Temperature
I-P Units
804 Feet
BAROMETRIC PRESSURE:29.062 IN. HG

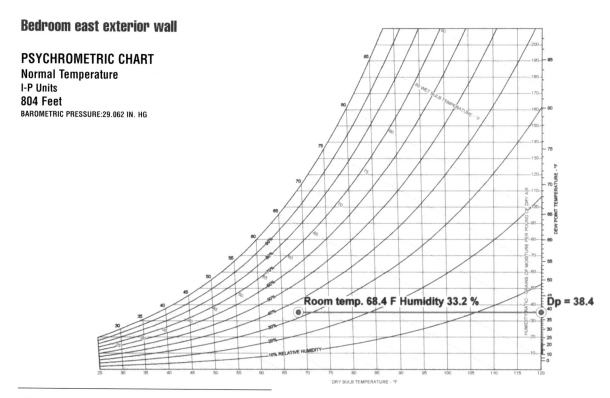

Room temp. 68.4 F Humidity 33.2 % Dp = 38.4

[1] Dp = Dew Point Temperature
The temperature of moist air saturated at the same pressure and humidity ratio. Alternatively, more simply the temperature at which water vapor will begin to condense from a sample of air.

[2] Interstitial for this report means in the wall, or behind the drywall.

Core cut one-interior partition wall forensic evaluation

We applied destructive testing to a partition wall system. This wall served a partition wall between the bedroom and living room. The wall penetration was initiated in the bedroom.

Roughly, a one-foot wide by two-foot high section was cut and removed for exploratory purposes. The below are the digital images with explanation of this test cut.

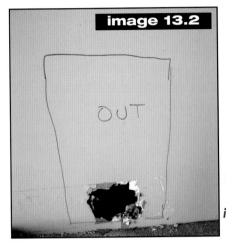

Roughly, one foot wide by two a high section was cut and removed. The existing penetration you see in the digital image was not conducted by REA INC. personnel.

After removing the first 5/8 inch drywall membrane, fungal reservoirs were encountered.

These fungal reservoirs could have not occurred through normal building science conditions.

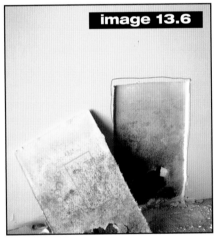

The cut member was turned to its backside. Fungal reservoirs can be seen on the backside of the outermost 5/8 inch drywall member.

The second 5/8 drywall membrane was removed and turned to its backside. The backside had glossy paint coating. Peeling back this glossy painted surface encountered additional fungal reservoirs.

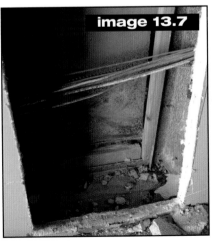

The interstitial space was exposed. Microbial reservoirs were seen in this interstitial space. The living room drywall wall was shimmed with wood members. New fungal reservoirs can be seen on the backside of this 1/2 inch drywall.

Core cut one-conclusion

Fungal reservoirs are old and concealed. It is our professional opinion that the fungal development processes was as follows:

- Leaks and poor building science cause the initial fungal reservoir manifestation and contamination. The entire condominium unit had to have been contaminated.
- The drywall was completely removed on the inside partition living room wall only leaving the exposed interstitial space, metal studs and the other bedroom 5/8 inch drywall side.
- The contaminated drywall on the inside partition bedroom wall was left intact. Fungal reservoirs existed on both sides of this membrane.
- Somebody painted the inner wall contaminated drywall with yellow paint covering the old fungal reservoirs. This task would have been easy due to the living room drywall membrane being removed.
- After the painting of the interstitial space, the partition living room wall was shimmed and new 5/8 drywall was added.

- The contaminated 5/8 inch drywall was covered with a second 5/8 inch drywall, concealing again the fungal reservoirs that existed on the exposed bedroom wall.
- Moisture was still not completely removed from this interstitial space during past construction phase. That is because new fungal reservoirs appeared on the new living room drywall backing and on the backside of the new 5/8 drywall backing in the bedroom. Fungal reservoirs were not seen on the interstitial painted surface. It is possible that the paint used had biocides or was mildew-proof type paint. X-ray fluorescence or other laboratory testing can be done to this member to determine its chemical content.

*NOTE: How does one put paint inside of a wall without removing one side?

*NOTE: How are fungal reservoirs trapped behind the yellow vapor retarding[3] paint?

Core cut two-interior partition wall forensic evaluation

We applied destructive testing to this wall system. This wall served a partition wall between the bedroom and living room. The wall penetration was initiated in the bedroom. Roughly, a one-foot wide by one-foot high section was cut and removed for exploratory purposes. This was duplicate of the core cut one to determine if fungal reservoirs existed between the two sandwiched 5/8 inch drywall members. The below are the digital images with explanations of this test cut.

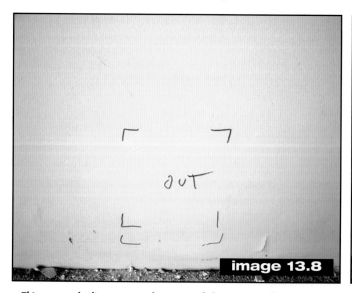

image 13.8

This was a duplicate cut to determine if the same conditions as core cut one exist. Both the core cut one and core cut two were conducted to an interior partition wall.

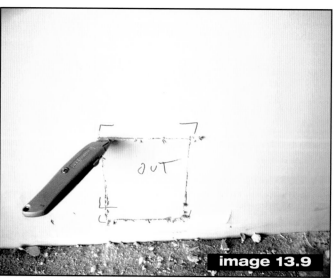

image 13.9

The 5/8 inch drywall was carefully cut out not to disturb the first and original construction 5/8 inch drywall layer.

---

[3] Vapor retarding means moisture and vapor diffusion cannot pass. We assumed this condition because the paint was glossy.

image 13.10

Once the specimens were cut, it was carefully removed for examination. Note: It is odd that two layers of 5/8 drywall was installed in a unit partition wall. Generally, two hour fire rating would be applied to the outer unit walls and not a center interior partition wall. All initial building blue prints should be reviewed to determine this condition.

image 13.11

Mold reservoirs were found on both membranes. This condition was not caused by vapor diffusion or depressurization. The initial drywall must have had the fungal reservoirs prior to the second 5/8 inch drywall installation. It was easy for new fungal reservoirs to develop on this outer and newer 5/8 inch drywall. This was an interior wall the would normally have the same environmental condition on both sides. The side cut was the bedroom and the opposite side was the living room. If by chance this space was depressurized, then the dew point would have formed on the interstitial painted side and not between the 5/8 inch bedroom drywall. The fungal reservoirs were present before this second layer of drywall was applied.

image 13.12

Tape lift taken for field microscope's evaluation. Field microscope on site for this evaluation. The theory here is, that when the new drywall was installed, the interstitial space still had moisture conditions that were desirable for additional amplification. Since the initial drywall layer had fungal reservoirs, then transfer and amplification would have not been difficult to occur.

image 13.13

Both core test one and two are sealed after exploratory investigation.

Core cut two-conclusion

The core cut two draws one conclusion. Fungal reservoir is old and was concealed. The same conclusions were drawn as were drawn in the core cut sample one.

Core cut three-interior partition wall forensic evaluation

We applied destructive testing to this wall system. This wall was the exterior wall in the living room. A wall penetration was done to determine the interstitial conditions.

Below are the digital images with explanations of this test cut.

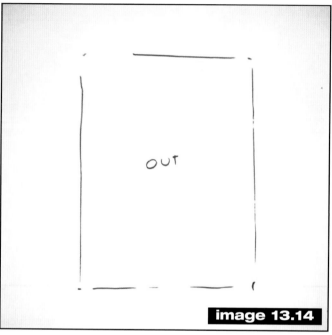

Roughly, an 7 inch wide by 12 inch long cut was conducted.

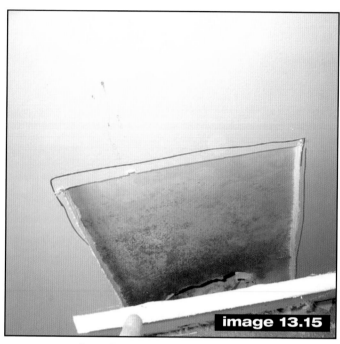

The wall was carefully cut, and removed.

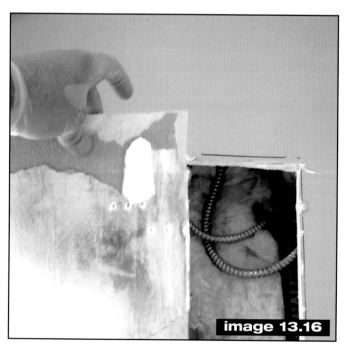

The drywall has a foil face that served as a vapor barrier.

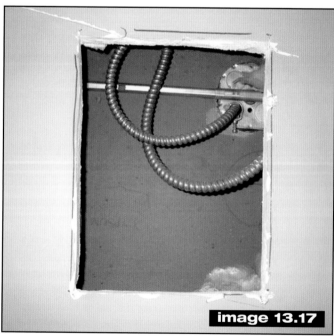

The insulation was removed. Notice the exterior outlet is not caulked to minimize air infiltration.

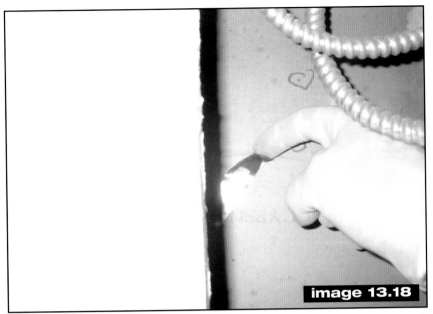

image 13.18

Small fungal reservoirs were observed in the intestinal space. These fungal reservoirs were seen on the outer gypsum board.

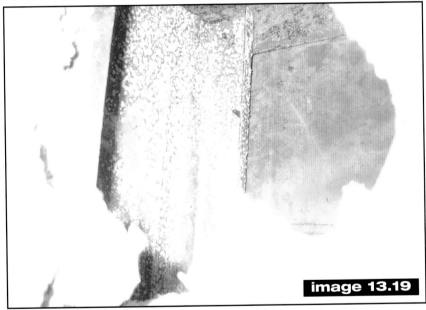

image 13.19

A second penetration was photographed that was cut by other parties. Fungal reservoirs were observed. From the digitals, one can see the severe corrosion of the metal stud. It takes significant moisture in this interstitial space for this type of corrosion to take place.

Core cut three-conclusion

The core cut three draws one conclusion. The sparse fungal spots were caused by vapor diffusion.[4] Exterior moist latent air during summer months travels into the interstitial exoskeleton wall. It is trapped and potentially condensates when the interior condominium air conditioning is running. The fungal reservoirs at this location were sparse. This was only one core cut and additional core cuts can be conducted to verify this condition. The wall penetration conducted by other parties draws several conclusions. The fungal reservoirs could have been caused by past envelope leaks or from vapor diffusion.

---

[4]Vapor diffusion only occurs when there is a pressure difference in walls or on either side of the building materials. When buildings are heated in cooled climates, the vapor pressure is higher inside the building than the outside. This means that the vapor pressure will travel from the interior to the exterior. The problem occurs when this vapor diffusion condition causes the moisture to condensate within the interstitial wall cavities. Similarly, when buildings are cooled in warm climates, the vapor pressure is higher on the outside of the building than that of the inside. This means that the vapor pressure will travel from the exterior to the interior. The problem once again occurs when this vapor diffusion condition causes the moisture to condensate within the interstitial wall cavities. The following are several examples when vapor diffusion occurs (see next page).

Additional digital images and explanations

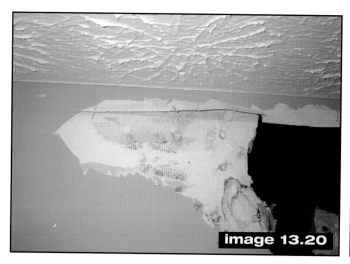

image 13.20

Fungal reserviors are found behind the paint on the interior of the condominum unit. We chipped the paint and peeled it back. These reserviors are old and have been covered.

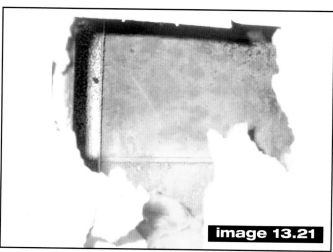

image 13.21

Fungal reservoirs are found behind the drywall on the exterior wall. It is our opinion that this condition is caused by past leaks and vapor diffusion. This condition may very well exist throughout the entire complex. It is advised to test other condominium units to determine the extent of this condition.

image 13.22

Fungal reservoirs under furnace.

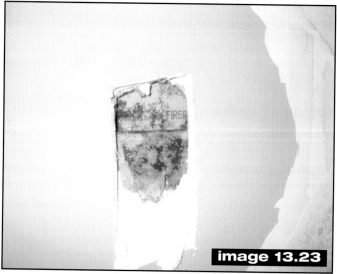

image 13.23

Fungal reservoir found under drywall in the kitchen above the countertop. Notice the fire rated drywall. This wall penetration was conducted by other consultants.

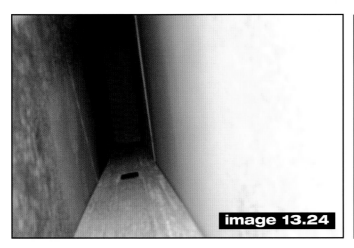

Digital image in intestinal wall cavity. This is the wall between the bedroom and living room. Fungal reservoirs seen on the living room drywall inner surface.

The ductwork system is faulty. These conditions cause pressurization and depressurization. These conditions lead to poor HVAC balancing. Poor HVAC balancing will cause undesirable conditions..

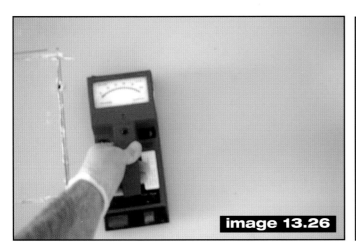

Moisture meter used for testing. Walls were dry at the time of inspection.

Moisture meter used for testing. Walls were dry at the time of inspection.

Moisture meter used for testing. Walls were dry at the time of inspection.

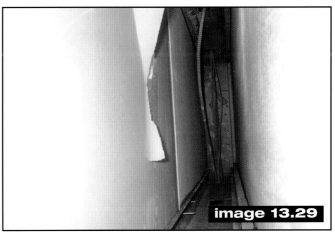

Intestinal digital image in wall between living room and bedroom. Notice the new drywall on the lower left side. Notice the microbial reservoirs on the right hand side.

Past leaks seen under carpet in bathroom. These past conditions have the probability of causing intestinal fungal reservoirs.

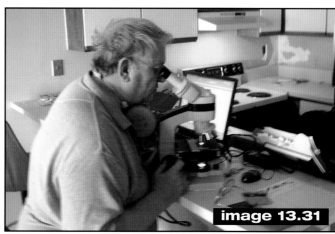

On site microscopic. Done for strategic laboratory sampling.

Past leak in closet. Dry today.

Forensic investigator wearing PPE.

EXECUTIVE SUMMARY [5]

It is our professional opinion with a high degree of certainty that,

1. This complex and / or condominium unit in question suffered major moisture events that led to microbial contamination.

2. This complex and / or condominium unit in question was not properly treated for microbial contamination in the past.

3. That this complex and / or condominium unit in question had several poor building science conditions, poor engineering designs, and faulty construction building products.

4. That this complex and / or condominium unit in question had previous experts that conducted extensive investigations and provided extensive scopes of work that may have not properly addressed microbial contamination.

5. That the present owner of this condominium unit was not informed of these major defects by all parties. Parties that knew of these defects were, building management, building executives, association members, other building condominium owners, past owners of this condominium unit, and all other professionals that were directly involved with past moisture events or repairs.

---

[5] The consultant reserves the right to change his opinion if additional facts are provided. The above conclusions were made from site inspection and evaluation. Inspector was not provided the entire history or all paperwork that existed with this unit or complex from conception.

Site Two Conditions

This was a four-unit apartment building. One of the lower units was vacant and a sewer backup occurred. The unit was left empty and microbial reservoirs amplified to the extreme.

Field Notes

Infrared surface temperature testing was done using a laser temperature testing apparatus. Testing was done to all interior and all exterior wall surfaces. Three exterior facing walls were tested. Each bar represents the average temperature of that wall. The average temperature of four tests were plotted on chart below.

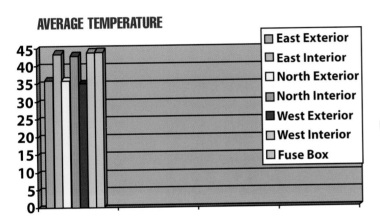

AVERAGE TEMPERATURE

- East Exterior
- East Interior
- North Exterior
- North Interior
- West Exterior
- West Interior
- Fuse Box

The exterior surface wall temperatures ranged from 35°F to 36°F. The interior surface wall temperature ranged from 43°F to 46°F.

Moisture & humidity mapping results

A second type of temperature testing was applied. This type of testing was done to achieve average room temperatures. The average of four tests per test location were documented below. Along with the average room temperatures, also tested was the relative humidity. Both temperature and relative humidity were tested using a sling psychrometer and a digital hygrometer. The sling psychrometer was used for baseline testing results and the digital hygrometer was used for the data collection. The following data represents these values.

Apartment unit east side	75.5% RH	53.7°F
Apartment unit west side	85.0% RH	49.0°F
Occupied 2nd floor above	62.0% RH	60.0°F
Not occupied 2nd unit	36.0% RH	60.0°F

Surface moisture testing was done on the slab-on-grade floor system. The moisture reading ranged from 14% - 16%. Surface wall moisture testing was done to most surfaces in the apartment unit, and found to be over 20% moisture content. All surface moisture mapping was conducted using the Tramex moisture-testing gauge.

Due to the high interior dwelling relative humidity, we applied psychrometric science to this entire first floor unit. The following data is a mathematical representation of temperature, humidity, and dew point in this first floor unit.

East side of first floor contaminated unit

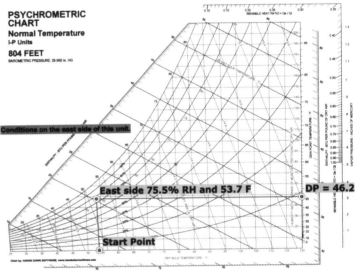

PSYCHROMETRIC CHART
Normal Temperature
I-P Units
804 FEET
BAROMETRIC PRESSURE: 29.062 in. HG

Conditions on the east side of this unit.

East side 75.5% RH and 53.7 F

DP = 46.2

Start Point

The above data means that all surfaces with temperature of 46.7°F and lower will condensate and form a dew point. From all our interior infrared laser temperature testing, all locations tested had surface temperatures less than 44.7°F. This is why all the exterior walls were wet and contaminated with fungal reservoirs. (Images 13.34 & 13.35)

image 13.34   image 13.35

West side of first floor contaminated unit

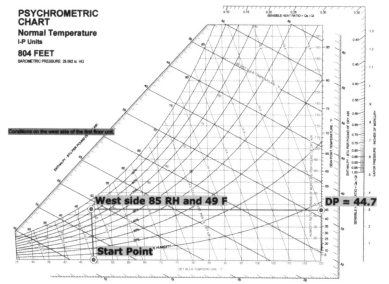

PSYCHROMETRIC CHART
Normal Temperature
I-P Units
804 FEET
BAROMETRIC PRESSURE: 29.062 in. HG

Conditions on the west side of the first floor unit.

West side 85 RH and 49 F

DP = 44.7

Start Point

Occupied unit above contaminated unit

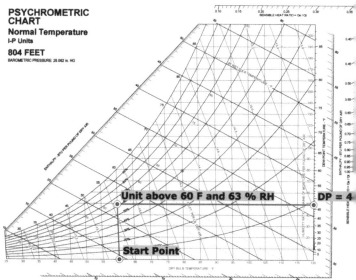

PSYCHROMETRIC CHART
Normal Temperature
I-P Units
804 FEET
BAROMETRIC PRESSURE: 29.062 in. HG

Unit above 60 F and 63 % RH

DP = 4

Start Point

The above data means that all surfaces with temperature of 44.7°F and lower will condensate and form a dew point. From all our interior infrared laser temperature testing, all locations tested had surface temperatures less than 44.7°F. This is why all the interior walls are wet and contaminated with fungal reservoirs. (Images 13.36 & 13.37)

The above data means that all surfaces with temperature of 44.0°F and lower will condensate and form a dew point. From all our interior infrared laser temperature testing, all locations tested had surface temperatures greater than 47.0°F, except window locations and one isolated outer colder wall. Due to surfaces not reaching dew points, fungal reservoir amplification was not abundant. The humidity levels are still high and not acceptable for winter months. Humidity or grains of moisture are traveling to this upper unit through vapor diffusion. (Image 13.38 & 13.39)

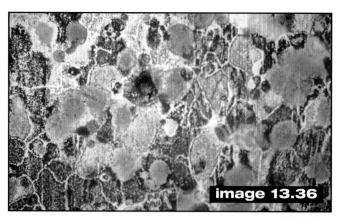

image 13.36

image 13.37

image 13.38

image 13.39

Unoccupied unit on the second floor north

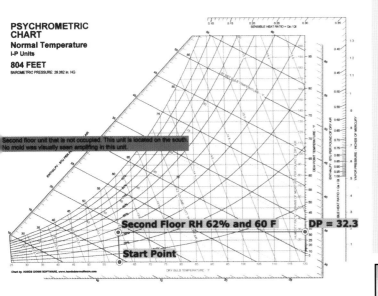

PSYCHROMETRIC
CHART
Normal Temperature
I-P Units

804 FEET
BAROMETRIC PRESSURE: 29.062 in. HG

Second floor unit that is not occupied. This unit is located on the south. No mold was visually seen amplifing in this unit.

Second Floor RH 62% and 60 F   DP = 32.3

Start Point

Chart by: HANDS DOWN SOFTWARE. www.handsdownsoftware.com

This unit has a low dew point and visual microbial amplification was not observed. This unit appeared to be recently painted and cleaned. (Images 13.40 & 13.41)

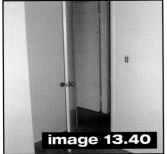

image 13.40

image 13.41

Due to the current high humidity level, moisture is condensating on the attic sheathing location. This condition is causing fungal reservoirs to amplify. We were able to gain access to one attic location from an access panel that existed in one bedroom. The following digital images were taken at this location.

image 13.42

image 13.43

EXECUTIVE SUMMARY

The lower unit located on the northeast side was vacant and locked. Both upper and lower units shared the same sanitary stack pipe. A large family occupied the upper unit. This family could easily discharge 100-200 gallons of gray water per day. Gray water would discharge and overflow out of the first floor drains. See the discharge overflow stains on the digital images[1] of the toilet and tub below. (Images 13.44 & 13.45)

This discharge would spread throughout the entire unit and become absorbed into the carpets through capillary action. The September month was warmer and significant evaporation occurred. The room was sealed tightly and evaporate could not escape. This evaporate became significant and saturated the air. Dew points were formed on all surfaces and severe microbial contamination was the result. This condition is now contributing to other conditions that exist within this building.

image 13.44

image 13.45

[1](Other digital images in are our electronic files .We use these images as notes for writing our conclusions. They are available only through paid depositions or additional reporting.)

Site Three Conditions

This was a new dwelling in a condominium complex. The new owners moved in and were irritated by the odors. The builder and other contractors could not determine the cause.

Scope

To determine or try to explain the following issues;
1. Indoor odor
2. Eye irritation

Field Notes

The following are field data from moisture and humidity mapping. This testing was done to determine if dwelling conditions would cause dew points or condensation. If dew points or condensation occurs, microbial reservoirs can develop. MVOC's, or microbial volatile organic compounds, are odors from the result of microbial reservoir amplification (musty smell).

Moisture & humidity mapping results

The entire home was mapped for room temperature, room humidity, surface temperatures, dew point, and moisture content. The sling psychrometer was used for baseline testing and the digital hygrometer was used for the data collection. All surface moisture mapping was conducted using the Tramex moisture-testing gauge. All surface temperature were taken using an infrared laser surface thermometer. All values are represented in mathematical terms, to determine if conditions exist that would promote fungal activity.

The entire home, with exception of attic, was investigated visually for microbial conditions. No significant visual microbial reservoirs were observed in these accessible areas.

We plotted the coldest location to view the graph for potential conditions (the coldest location during the inspection).

Basement unfinished room

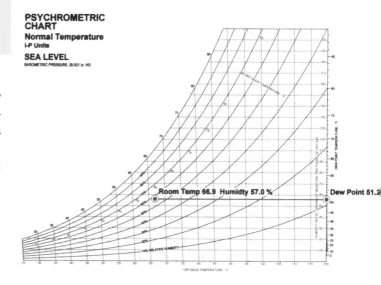

The above mathematical representation depicts that during our inspection, the dew point[1] for the above condition was 51.2°F. In conclusion, the basement conditions or upper house conditions did not have moisture levels or humidity levels that would cause a dew point today. Dew point and moisture are necessary for microbial amplification. This data can change from day to day. This data does not depict all present or past interstitial[2] conditions.

Location	Ambient Temperature °F	RH%	Dew Point	Interior wall Temperature °F	Floor Temperature °F	Ceiling Temperature °F
Basement finished room	67.7	57.3	51.6	65.0	65.0	68.3
Basement un-finished room	66.9	57.0	51.2	66.0	59.0	68.2
Living room	67.9	57.0	51.2	67.0	67.0	68.0
Master bedroom	69.6	55.0	52.7	68.0	68.0	70.0
Other bedroom	70.0	53.4	52.1	68.0	68.3	71.0

[1]DP = Dew Point Temperature. The temperature of moist air saturated at the same pressure and humidity ratio. Alternatively, more simply the temperature at which water vapor will begin to condense from a sample of air.

[2]Interstitial for this report means in the wall, or behind the drywall.

Odor testing

Due to unknown origin of odor, odor testing was conducted using a Sensidyne[3] portable odor monitor (Image 13.46). The gauge does not distinguish exactly what causes the odor. The gauge measures total odor counts, and is used to determine if odor concentrations are higher at certain locations. Furthermore, the gauge values will be slightly different depending on zero calibration. For this report. we can consider values less than 137 to be significantly less odoriferous than values of 137 and greater. From the results obtained, odor levels were generally higher when the HVAC systems were operating. The counts of exterior odor or zero calibration was 137 counts. The odors increased to 205 when entering the dwelling. The odors increased to 215 after the HVAC system is energized. The conclusion to this data is that the energized HVAC system is intensifying odor.

Due to the above determination, the HVAC system was visually evaluated. It was determined that the basement is being depressurized and the upper floor is being pressurized. Our conclusion is strictly visual. A full blower door or infiltrometer test would be needed to quantify.

HVAC and building science

Indoor air quality, fungal problems, bacterial problems, and odors arise in residential buildings when there is inadequate ventilation air or contaminated air introduced into the indoor environment. The home's HVAC system was not balanced. The basement supply vents were closed and the return vents were infiltrating air. Most of the upper home's return air vents were not working and the basement was being depressurized. When depressurized, makeup air must come from somewhere. This air can comes from makeup air vents. Many times this air comes in, through downdrafts from the furnace, hot water heater, or fireplace. Finally, makeup air can come from sumps, cracks, walls, vapor barrior leaks and other penetrations.

The use of smoke tubes was implemented during this investigation. It was determined that the some of the makeup air was coming from the sump pump pit (Image 13.47). This sump pump pit had a drain tile that went to the exterior soil. This exterior soil had limestone. The limestone at the drain tile elevation may have been saturated due to geological conditions and adjacent lake elevation. This limestone had a stone odor that is being infiltrated into the HVAC system from return air duct leakage or infiltration.

Digital images

image 13.46

Sensidyne portable odor monitor readings during HVAC operation. The readings increase after the HVAC system was energized.

image 13.47

Smoke tube shows that air is being pulled out of sump pump pit. The blue pipe is the drain tile. Limestone and aggregate surround this drain tile.

---

[3]This instrument detects the presence of substances by the measurement of the intensity of electrical and thermal effects, which occur when a substance contacts a heated, semi conduction, metal oxide coated, and platinum coil – the sensor.

image 13.48

Smoke is being sucked into cold air return from poor filter cover. This filter is too big for this ductwork.

image 13.49

Smoke is being sucked into cold air return. This location has no end cap and the entire crawl space is being depressurized.

image 13.50

Smoke is being sucked or infiltrated into the cold air return. This is due to return air duct leakage. Many locations throughout the basement have poorly sealed ducts.

image 13.51

Smoke being sucked or infiltrated into the cold air return that is missing an end cap in the crawl location. This missing end cap member is not allowing for upper floor cold air returns to operate.

Window well full of limestone. No cover exists at this location.

Moisture stain from the limestone filled window well in crawl space. The moisture meter shows that moisture is migrating inward.

Consultant is performing combustion analysis to eliminate the carbon monoxide potential.

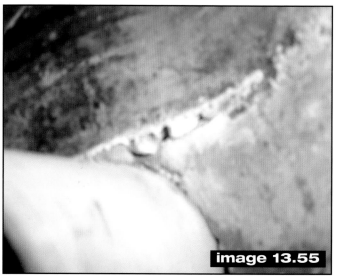

One can see the limestone that surrounds the pit at this excessive well penetration.

EXECUTIVE SUMMARY

1. It is our professional opinion with reasonable certainty, that, odors in this home are intensified by a poorly installed and poorly balanced HVAC system.

2. It is our professional opinion with reasonable certainty, that full HVAC diagnostics are needed. Diagnostics data needs to be interpreted so a scope of work can be generated. The scope of work should include duct reconstruction, duct sealing, air balancing, and building engineering changes.

3. Finally, is our professional opinion with reasonable certainty that the odor and eye irritation[4] that people in this dwelling experience, is contributed by the sucking of wet subsurface soil aggregate.

[4]Eye irritation should be diagnosed by a doctor. We are only assuming that eye irritation is correlated with odors. We are not health specialist nor claim to be. All sensitivity conditions must be analyzed by an allergen or toxicologist.

Site Four

This is a condominium unit in a high-rise building. The upper unit had a moisture event. The lower unit now has discolored tile and potential moisture conditions.

Scope

To determine if the past moisture event in the kitchen was still active. We were informed that building management had made repairs and adjustments to pacify this condition. To the best of their knowledge and quality control, they felt the moisture condition was no longer occurring.

Site Conditions

1. Microbial reservoirs on kitchen wall from past roof leak
2. Moisture stains on and in kitchen wall from past roof leak
3. Floor tile conditions; Inner wall conditions; Roof top conditions

Field notes

The following are field data from moisture and humidity mapping. Calculation of the dew point was only conducted to one kitchen location. See the highlighted yellow section below.

Moisture & humidity mapping results

The condominium unit was partially mapped for room temperature, room humidity, surface temperatures, and moisture content. The sling psychrometer was used for baseline testing results and the digital hygrometer was used for the data collection. All surface moisture mapping was conducted using the Tramex moisture-testing gauge and an infrared laser thermometer. All values are represented in mathematical terms to determine potential cause of fungal development. The entire home with exception of attic was investigated visually for microbial conditions. No significant visual microbial reservoirs were observed at these accessible areas.

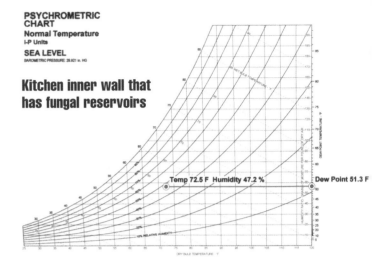

PSYCHROMETRIC CHART
Normal Temperature
I-P Units
SEA LEVEL
BAROMETRIC PRESSURE: 29.921 in. HG

Kitchen inner wall that has fungal reservoirs

Temp 72.5 F   Humidity 47.2 %   Dew Point 51.3 F

The above mathematical representation depicts that during our inspection, the dew point for the above condition was 51.3°F. In conclusion, the unit's conditions did not have moisture levels nor did it have humidity levels that would cause dew points today. Dew points[1] and moisture are usually essential for microbial manifestation or amplification. This data can change from day to day. This data does not depict all present, or present interstitial[2] conditions.

image 13.56

image 13.57

Location	Ambient Temperature °F	RH%	Dew Point	Interior wall Temperature °F	Floor Temperature °F	Ceiling Temperature °F
Family room	68.6	51.2	65.2	69.6	71	71.8
Living room	68.9	49.6	70.2	71.4	72.6	72.8
Dining room	70.4	46.8	69.8	71.8	72.4	72.4
Kitchen slight fungal activity	72.5	47.2	68.8	72.6	73.4	73.6
Bedroom	71.8	43.7	70	72.2	72.8	72.6
Rear closet	72	44.9	72.8	73	72.8	72.4
Exterior prior to rain; cloudy	65.3	62	na	na	na	na

[1]DP = Dew Point Temperature. The temperature of moist air saturated at the same pressure and humidity ratio. Alternatively, more simply the temperature at which water vapor will begin to condense from a sample of air.

[2]Interstitial for this report means in the wall, or behind the drywall.

The following a are several digital images taken at the dwelling. Below these images is an explanation of condition.

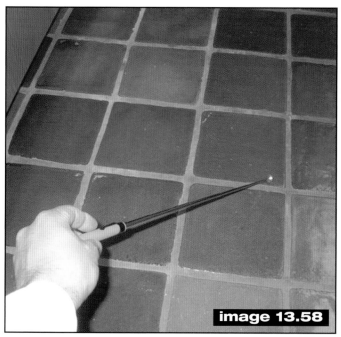

image 13.58

Sounding of initial floor. The initial floor installation did not have 100% bond. Many tiles were not properly bonded to sub-floor. The past leak had easy access below the tile system.

image 13.59

The darker floor tile is the moist area from the past leak. Moisture was trapped below the this tile. If the tile system was properly installed, the leak would have not traveled under the floor tile.

image 13.60

The was a dry area that was tested using a probe moisture meter. This is done to calibrate the gauge and form a base line. The gauge was moved to the darker color tile areas. These areas had moisture levels that indicated some slight moisture from the past event still existed. The management indicated that they had been watching this area and tiles have been slowly drying.

image 13.61

This was a wet area using a surface moisture meter. This location still had some slight moisture present. We always use several different test gauges to back up all our results and conclusions.

image 13.62

The wall that once leaked was found to be dry at the time of inspection. Testing was done using a surface moisture meter.

image 13.63

The wall that once leaked was found to be dry at the time of inspection. Testing was done using a second surface moisture meter.

EXECUTIVE SUMMARY

1. It is our professional opinion with reasonable certainty that the most resent moisture event that existed in the kitchen wall has ceased or is not leaking today. (From the results of our investigation, it was assumed that the roof had a past leak. After inspection of the rooftop, it was determined that the past roof leak had been addressed. We did point out several small concern locations to the management at that time.)

2. It is our professional opinion with reasonable certainty, that if the floor had been properly installed, moisture would have not have migrated beneath.

3. It is our professional opinion with reasonable certainty, that temperature and humidity conditions today will not promote microbial amplification in this unit. (The unit does have wallpaper conditions that could promote microbial development if interior conditions permit. This type of investigation was not part of the scope of this inspection. Vinyl wallpaper on exterior walls has the potential to create undesirable vapor barrier conditions if certain conditions permit.)

image 13.64

image 13.65

Site Five

This was a home that had microbial reservoirs on the attic sheathing. A mold remediator came to this home and sprayed the attic with paint. Several years later, the mold came back and the attic paint started to peel.

Site Conditions

1. Microbial contamination on attic sheathing.
2. Indoor environment that promotes microbial development and amplification.

Field Notes

The following are field data from moisture and humidity mapping. We only calculated the dew point at one of the below samples. The attic south lower roof was the coldest at 56.6°F and was plotted to determine and view projected dew point.

Moisture & humidity mapping results

The entire home was mapped for room temperature, room humidity, surface temperatures, and moisture content. The sling psychrometer was used for baseline testing results and the digital hygrometer was used for the data collection. All surface moisture mapping was conducted using the Tramex moisture-testing gauge and an infrared laser. All values are represented in mathematical terms to determine potential cause of fungal development.

image 13.66

Location	Ambient temperature °F	RH%	Exterior wall temperature °F	Interior wall temperature °F	Floor temperature °F	Ceiling temperature °F
Living room	69.3	58.3	69.4	77.8	78.6	78.6
Basement	72.7	49.8	59.8	71.2	68.4	71.8
Living room	72.9	53.2	66.6	79.6	75.2	75.8
Second floor office front	74.2	52.3	71.2	74.6	75.6	74.6
Bedroom rear	75.1	49.8	73.4	75	76.2	75.2
Attic	65.7	55.6	57.2			
			66.0			
			65.6 north			
			66 north			
			66.4 north			
			66.4			
Exterior 1:00 PM	54.5	70.9	na	na	na	na

Attic sheathing mold and peeling paint

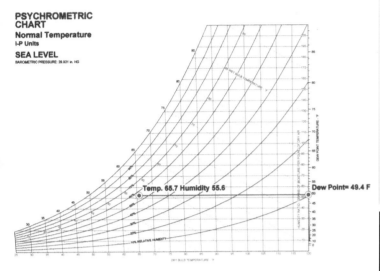

PSYCHROMETRIC
CHART
Normal Temperature
I-P Units

SEA LEVEL
BAROMETRIC PRESSURE: 29.921 in. HG

Temp. 65.7 Humidity 55.6   Dew Point= 49.4 F

EXECUTIVE SUMMARY

During our inspection, the humidifier was not running. We were informed that this unit is used frequently during the winter months. This unit will produce humidity every time the furnace fan turns on. It is possible, that this unit operates during other seasons as well. The basement also has a furnace that does not have a connected cold air return. The furnace causes depressurization of the basement level. This depressurization condition sucks moisture from the slab and foundation walls. Vapor diffusion[3] occurs much faster when areas are depressurized. This attic is tight and cannot handle the humidity this home and furnace humidifier produce. The home produces so much moisture that the moisture condensates on all cold surfaces that are below their respective dew points. This is why fungal reservoirs exist on the attic sheathing.

image 13.69

The above mathematical representation depicts that during our inspection, the dew point for the above condition was 49.4°F. In conclusion, the attic conditions did not have moisture levels nor did it have humidity levels that would cause dew points today. Dew points[1] and moisture are necessary for microbial amplification. This data can change from day to day. This data does not depict all present interstitial[2] conditions or all past interstitial conditions. In the wintertime, when the attic sheathing conditions sustain lower temperatures, dew points will have a high probability in occurring.

image 13.70

image 13.67

image 13.68

[1]DP = Dew Point Temperature. The temperature of moist air saturated at the same pressure and humidity ratio. Alternatively, more simply the temperature at which water vapor will begin to condense from a sample of air.

[2]Interstitial for this report means in the wall, or behind the drywall.

[3]Vapor diffusion is a H_2O or water vapor state moving through porous materials that do not contain vapor barriers or retarders such as concrete, drywall, wood and other.

In the past, a contractor removed the attic sheathing fungal reservoirs. It was at that time, that the entire attic structure was encapsulated with a paint film membrane that contained a biocide. Today, this paint is falling and fungal reservoirs are once again amplifying. This reoccurring condition was inevitable, because the moisture sources were not ceased. Humidity or water vapor travels into this attic space and condensates on the sheathing. It causes the sheathing to expand. This fails the paint membrane. This is why paint chips exist on the attic floor.

Indoor humidity control should be the primary means to limit moisture accumulation in the attic. This home is built in a colder climate region and adequate attic ventilation should not be the only safeguard to control moisture. The attic ventilation does help control heat in summer months and ice dam formation in winter months. At this time, the attic ventilation is also not adequate.

The following are the measures that would make attic condensation and fungal amplification more passive.

1. Minimize humidifier use on furnace.
2. Install a cold air return and balance the heating system.
3. Strategically add attic ventilation.
4. Use a basement dehumidifier during peak humid times.

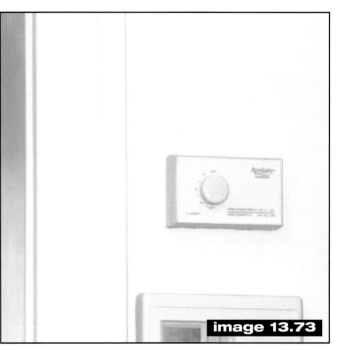

image 13.73

image 13.71

image 13.72

Site Six

Home had mold growing in the corner of the living room. Infrared surface temperature testing was done to all living room surfaces.

Field Notes

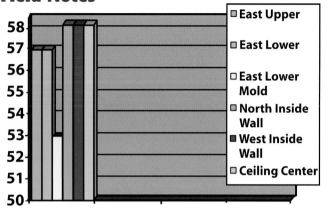

Legend:
- East Upper
- East Lower
- East Lower Mold
- North Inside Wall
- West Inside Wall
- Ceiling Center

In the bar chart above, the surface temperature ranged from 53°F to 58°F. The colder temperatures were found on the lower east wall. This area will tend to be colder due to minimal sun exposure. Morning sun is blocked by the apartment buildings, a brick front wall and by a tree. The coldest temperature of 53°F was at the mold reservoirs located at the lower southeast corner behind the CD rack.

image 13.74

image 13.75

The above digital images are mold reservoirs on walls and a cassette air test for mold spores.

Infrared surface temperature testing was done to all north west bedroom surfaces. The surface temperature ranged from 55°F to 60°F. The colder temperatures were found on the upper southwest corner ceiling. This area will tend to be colder due to minimal sun exposure. The sun blocks this corner due to the roofing system and roof overhang. The coldest temperatures of 53°F were at the mold reservoirs located at upper southwest corner on the ceiling. Image 13.76 is from the bedroom ceiling of the north west bedroom.

Other infrared surface temperature testing was conducted in other dwelling locations. These values are not of concern at this point, other than a documentation of field data.

The temperature was colder in the non-conditioned garage and attic. The exterior temperature was 44.3°F. Most conditioned home surface temperatures are roughly 60°F. We were only concerned with the lower temperatures that were taken at the two visual mold reservoir locations in the conditioned living space...

image 13.76

Moisture & humidity mapping results

A second type of temperature testing conducted was average room temperatures. Unlike the surface temperature testing, these temperatures were taken in the center of the dwelling rooms. These temperatures were taken using a sling psychrometer and an electronic gauge. The following chart lists the average room temperatures in this dwelling with their respective relative humidity readings.

ROOM	AVERAGE TEMP	RELATIVE HUMIDITY
• Basement	68.0°F	50.2%
• Kitchen	69.0°F	48.0%
• Living Room	71.0°F	52.0%
• Bedroom	71.0°F	52.0%
• Bedroom	72.0°F	53.0%
• Bedroom	73.6°F	52.0%
• Exterior	44.3°F	46.0%

The interior humidity readings were high and excessive with respect to the colder winter months. The humidifier on the furnace was set to 45% today. A sign was seen on the furnace that stated, "Set to 45% in winter" (Image 13.77). This is bad advice, and high dwelling humidity is the result. Due to the high dwelling relative humidity, we applied psychrometric science to the two mold locations on the first floor. The following data is a mathematical representation of temperature, humidity, and dew point in the main living room.

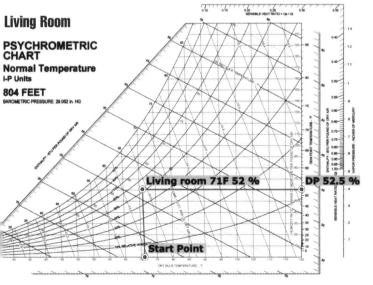

Living Room

PSYCHROMETRIC CHART
Normal Temperature
I-P Units
804 FEET
BAROMETRIC PRESSURE: 29.082 in. HG

Living room 71F 52 %   DP 52.5 %   Start Point

The upper graph is important as it shows the dew point. The dew point is what is causing the microbial reservoir condition in the living room. The upper graph is the mathematical representation of the living room conditions at approximately 10:00 AM on the day of the investigation. All above temperature readings were taken simultaneously within a 5-minute period. The graph shows that the dew point in the living room is exactly 52.5°F with the 71°F average room temperature and 52% average relative humidity. All surfaces that are exactly 52.5°F or lower will condensate. The front door glass was condensating and was found to have 51°F interior glass temperatures. This lower southeast corner wall location is the coldest location in this living room, and it condensates first and is most likely to harbor mold reservoirs.

The same hold true for the northwest bedroom ceiling.

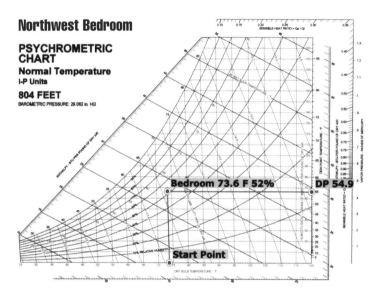

Northwest Bedroom

PSYCHROMETRIC CHART
Normal Temperature
I-P Units
804 FEET
BAROMETRIC PRESSURE: 29.082 in. HG

Bedroom 73.6 F 52%   DP 54.9   Start Point

The upper graph is important as it shows the dew point. The dew point is what is causing the microbial reservoir condition in the north west bedroom. The upper graph is the mathematical representation of the bedroom conditions at approximately 10:05 AM on the day of the investigation. All temperature readings were taken simultaneously within a 5-minute period. The graph shows that the dew point in the bedroom is exactly 54.9°F with the 73.6°F average room temperature and 52% average relative humidity. All surfaces that are exactly 54.9°F or lower will condensate. The bottom window glass was slightly condensating and was 54°F. The mold was amplifying in the coldest location in this room, which was the upper ceiling location. This ceiling location condensates first and is most likely to harbor mold reservoirs.

image 13.77

image 13.78

image 13.79

image 13.80

image 13.81

image 13.82

If humidity and temperature are not controlled soon in the dwelling, the home may become severely contaminated with fungal reservoirs.

Other moisture conditions that exist at this dwelling. The following conditions are potential moisture contributors. They are not significant to the present indoor conditions. These items were simply observations and were not part of our scope of work. These items are as follows; *1) The foundation walls have cracks. Moisture entry is possible at these locations. 2) The building brick fascia has some cracks and sill is improperly sloped. Interstitial conditions can occur. The brick fascia also lack weep holes. 3) The roofing system is old and small penetration cracks are occurring. One location has a missing shingle. 4) The furnace system is not balanced. 5) The bathroom has no fan. 6) Some gutters have ice dams. 7) Some gutters are overflowing and not properly sloped. 8) The north sunroom is not watertight and may have leaks due to condition and design. 9) Due to high indoor humidity, the attic is now susceptible to mold reservoir conditions due to potential dew points. 10) Trees are located near this dwelling and tree root conditions* are possible. *11) The attic has some moisture rip stains from possible sheathing condensation. 12) The filter is dirty and will cause a pressure drop, which could contribute to depressurization. 13) Tree roots if they exist in underground drains can contribute to basement conditions. 14) Downspouts are not properly maintained. All items above are areas that require maintenance and moisture control. These conditions are generally common and frequently found in most dwellings. (We reserve the right to comment on other photos that were taken and not added to this report. Total of 150 digital images exist in our files. All 150 photos were used to make our conclusions. The photos are considered our notes. Photos can be purchased for additional fees or through paid depositions.)*

EXECUTIVE SUMMARY High humidity conditions in this dwelling are causing microbial reservoirs to amplify. High humidity is being generated by the continually running furnace humidifier. Instructions placed on the furnace are not accurate and jeopardizing the health of this home.

Site Seven

Home has a sick child and numerous microbial reservoirs.

Site Conditions

The following are obvious fungal reservoirs that were observed during the investigation. We did not perform interstitial investigations today. Interstitial conditions have a have a high probability to exist at numerous locations.

1. Microbial reservoirs on basement corner in basement bedroom.
2. Microbial reservoirs on carpet and under carpet in basement east side.
3. Microbial reservoirs on basement portion wall found in furnace room and well tank closet.
4. Microbial reservoirs on basement timbers on bracing and joists.
5. Microbial reservoirs on east living room at chimney.
6. Microbial reservoirs on attic sheathing on east side.
7. Microbial reservoirs on ceiling drywall on north side, in attic under insulation.

Field Notes

The following are field data from moisture and humidity mapping. Calculation of the dew point was only conducted for one location. See the highlighted yellow section below.

Moisture & humidity mapping results

The entire home was mapped for room temperature, room humidity, surface temperatures, and moisture content. The sling psychrometer was used for baseline testing results and the digital hygrometer was used for the data collection. All surface moisture mapping was conducted using the Tramex moisture-testing gauge and an infrared laser. All values are represented in mathematical terms to determine potential cause of fungal development.

We plotted this area because it was wet to the touch. This area was the wet corner in the black colored bedroom. We also plotted this location due to it being the coldest spot in the home.

Bedroom in the wet corner

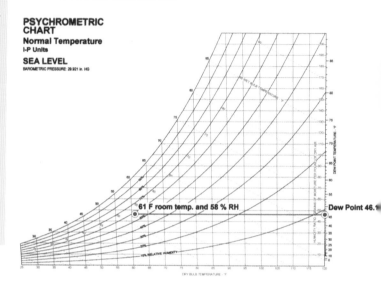

PSYCHROMETRIC CHART
Normal Temperature I-P Units
SEA LEVEL
BAROMETRIC PRESSURE: 29.921 in. HG

61 F room temp. and 58 % RH

Dew Point 46.1

The above mathematical representation depicts that during our inspection, the dew point for the above condition was 46.1°F. In conclusion, the basement conditions did not have moisture levels nor did it have humidity levels that would cause dew points today. Dew points and moisture are necessary for microbial amplification. This data can change from day to day. The above-plotted location was wet from active exterior leaks. It is my professional opinion that if changes are not made, during winter months, numerous home locations will sustain dew point condensation conditions.

Location	Ambient temp. °F	RH%	Dew Point	Surface of mold temperature °F	Other temp. °F	Other temp. °F
Basement	61.8	58.0	33.4	Behind carpet on east 62.0 Closet base drywall 66.5 Bedroom wet corner 52.0-56.0 Shower wall 62.5	Floor 64.0	Upper Wall 67.0
Master	68.3	55.4	51.9	NA	NA	NA
Kitchen	67.7	53.3	49.7	NA		
Dining room	67.0	51.6	47.9	NA	Floor 64.0	Inner Wall 65.0
Living room	66.4	50.4	47.0	East wall near fireplace 62.5	Outer Door 64.5	Ceiling 65.0
Front bed	66.6	49.5	47.2	NA	NA	NA
Exterior	54.5	47.8	36.6	NA Attic mold on east side of home 66.0 Attic mold on north side of home under insulation and under 6mil plastic 61.0		

The following are several digital images taken at the dwelling. Below these images is explanation of condition.

image 13.83

Microbial reservoirs on basement corner in basement bedroom. The exterior at this location is poorly maintained. The brick missing weep holes, the mulch too high, the brick interface not sealed, poor drainage exists, and downspout not properly connected are all contributors to the fungal reservoirs in this basement bathroom.

image 13.84

Microbial reservoirs on basement corner in basement bedroom. The results of the exterior conditions are causing microbial reservoir manifestation and amplification. The probability of interstitial contamination exists behind these drywall walls. This room also has obvious musty odors. This condition is active and deterioration will continue.

image 13.85

Microbial reservoirs on basement portion wall found in furnace room and well tank closet. These reservoirs are caused by vapor diffusion, foundation wall seepage or aggressive wet carpet cleaning or past events.

image 13.86

Microbial reservoirs on basement portion wall found in furnace room and well tank closet. These reservoirs are caused by vapor diffusion, foundation wall seepage or aggressive wet carpet cleaning or past events.

image 13.87

Microbial reservoirs on basement timbers on bracing and joists. These reservoirs are generally caused by initial construction or wet basement during construction.

image 13.88

Microbial reservoirs on attic sheathing seen on the east side. These reservoirs are caused by dew point condensation during winter months. The indoor home humidity is too high, and needs to be controlled.

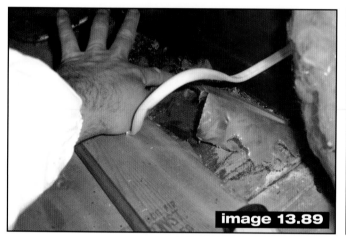

image 13.89

Microbial reservoirs are hidden under ceiling vapor barrier. This was the cause of vapor diffusion, poor building science and possible past ice dam conditions. The indoor humidity must be controlled.

image 13.90

Microbial reservoirs in living room ceiling from past chimney leaks, or vapor diffusion, or ice. Past repairs were seen at this location.

image 13.91

Sump pump sludge needs further evaluation.

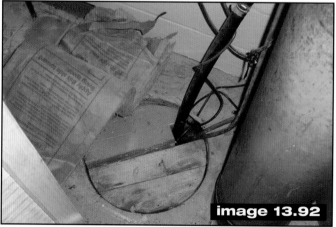

image 13.92

Mold from condensation on water purifying and sump pump cover.

Wet surrounding property. These conditions contribute to a moist geographical location.

Microbial reservoirs inside a closet wall in the basement location.

Major contributor to high indoor air humidity. These units can cause winter condensation and dew point conditions.

Microbial reservoirs from typical shower leaks.

EXECUTIVE SUMMARY

It is our professional opinion, with reasonable professional certainty;

- that, past events such as ice dams, plumbing leaks and other leaks have caused microbial reservoir to manifest
- that, certain building conditions and certain building science conditions are causing microbial reservoirs to manifest
- that, that several poor maintenance condition and poor repairs are causing microbial reservoirs to manifest

- that, this home has conditions that permit microbial amplification
- that airflows, fans, HVAC and other conditions may be causing depressurization of certain locations
- and finally, if maintenance, changes, remediation, and moisture control are not implemented, microbial amplification will augment.

SAMPLE BUILDING SCIENCE REPORT

Site Notes/Psychrometric/Moisture Building Science

Site Conditions

1. Significant moisture, fungal reservoirs, and frost accumulation on the attic sheathing, 2X4 trusses, sidewalls, and attic metal vents.
2. Significant fungal reservoirs on walls and ceilings of the second floor bathroom.
3. Fungal reservoirs in master bedroom closet and from the wall in dormer location.
4. New furnace and old humidifier repaired.

Moisture & humidity mapping results

The entire home was mapped for room temperature, room humidity, surface temperatures, and moisture content. The sling psychrometer was used for baseline testing results and the digital hygrometer was used for the data collection. All surface moisture mapping was conducted using the Tramex moisture-testing gauge. All values are represented in mathematical terms to determine cause of fungal amplification.

The attic sheathing and sidewalls were wet and had fungal reservoirs. The first set of bars labeled RmT[3] represents the room temperature in Fahrenheit. The second group of bars represents the room's relative humidity[4] in percent. The third set of bars represents the infrared laser surface temperature reading in Fahrenheit. Surface moisture testing of the sheathing was also done. The sheathing was found to be saturated.

Due to the high attic relative humidity, we applied Psychrometric Science. The data is a mathematical representation of temperature, humidity, and dew point of the attic condition at the time of inspection. See graph on page 93.

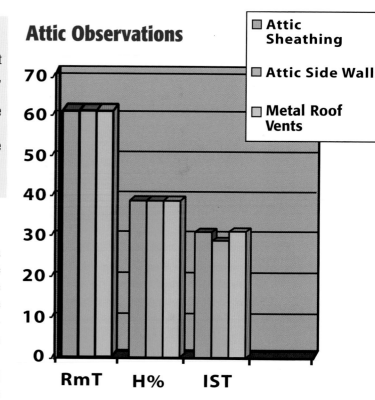

Attic Observations

Legend:
- Attic Sheathing
- Attic Side Wall
- Metal Roof Vents

Y-axis: 0, 10, 20, 30, 40, 50, 60, 70

X-axis: RmT, H%, IST

Metal Roof Vents

image 13.97

---

[3] RT = Room Temp + Dry-Bulb Temperature
The temperature of air read on a standard thermometer indicating its thermal state.

[4] H% = Percent Relative Humidity
The ratio of mole fraction of water vapor in a given moist air sample to the mole fraction in a saturated air sample at the same temperature and pressure.

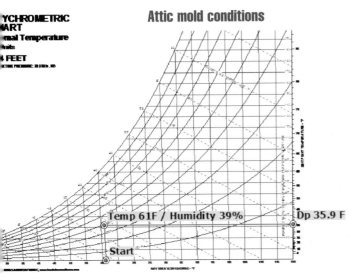

Attic mold conditions

PSYCHROMETRIC CHART
Normal Temperature
Units
FEET

Temp 61F / Humidity 39%   Dp 35.9 F

Start

Master Bedroom Observation

The master bedroom closet and one wall had fungal reservoirs. Surface moisture testing was also done to the fungal reservoir locations. These two areas were found to have over 20 percent moisture content. The moisture meter is highest reading is 20 percent. Surface moisture readings of 16 percent and greater are desirable for fungal amplification.

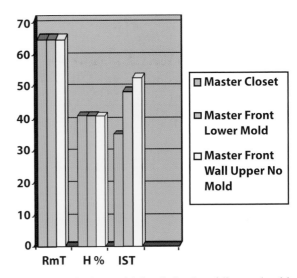

The above mathematical representation depicts that during the inspection the **attic dew point**[5] **was 35.9°F**. This means that the humidity in the attic is condensating on all surfaces that are 35.9°F. All surfaces in the attic were below this 35.9°F value at the time of inspection. The attic sheathing was 31.1°F, the attic end walls were 29°F, and the metal roof vents were 29°F with the emmisivity[6] correction. All locations in the attic were wet and condensating. These conditions are causing fungal amplification.

Due to the bedroom high relative humidity, and cold wall temperatures, we applied Psychrometric Science. The following data is a mathematical representation of temperature, humidity, and dew point. (See graph on p.94).

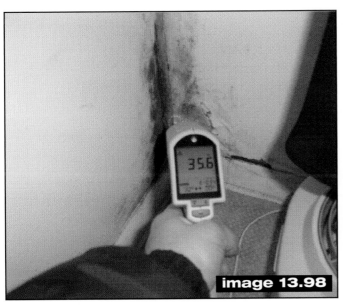

image 13.98

image 13.99

[5] Dp = Dew Point Temperature
The temperature of moist air saturated at the same pressure and humidity ratio. Alternatively, more simply the temperature at which water vapor will begin to condense from a sample of air.

[6] This is a correction factor on your laser infrared thermometer. It must be corrected when testing metal, shiny surfaces, glass or ect.

The adjoining mathematical representation depicts that the closet dew point is 40.8°F. This means that the humidity is causing condensation at all surfaces that are 40.8°F. and below. The wall was cold in the closet at 35.6°F. The bedroom wall was cold and was 48.6°F. This was not cold enough today to cause a dew point. At these locations, the walls were the coldest. This means that dew points will form and cause condensation. Condensation will cause fungal reservoirs to develop and fungal amplification is inevitable.

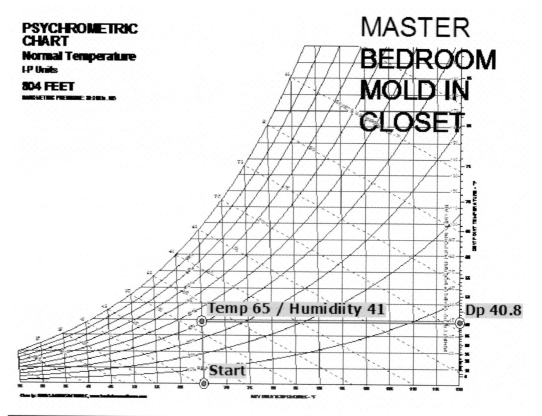

PSYCHROMETRIC CHART
Normal Temperature
I-P Units
804 FEET

MASTER BEDROOM MOLD IN CLOSET

Temp 65 / Humidiity 41 — Dp 40.8

Start

image 13.100

Field Notes

The following are field data from mapping. We only calculated the dew points at the fungal reservoir locations.

Location	Room Temp	Room RH%	Surface Temp
Fr Bedroom	64.8	45.1	61
Rr Bedroom	70	38	64
Fr Bedroom	65	41	53
2nd Fl Bath	65	44	55
Rr Bedroom	66	41	55
2nd Hall	66	41	63
Bsmt	63	35	62
Dining	67	40	58
Living	68	38	60
Garage attic	59	19	23
Garage Rm	59	19	24
Basement	63	35	62
Crawl	63	35	54
OUTSIDE	24	35	21 ON SIDING
CLOSET MOLD	**65**	**41**	**35.6**
WALL MOLD	**65**	**41**	**48.6**
ATTIC MOLD	**61**	**39**	**31**
BATH MOLD	**65**	**44**	**55**

Other Moisture Sources

The home consists of a large family of seven. We were informed that the family takes five to six showers daily, ten plus laundry loads weekly, ten plus dishwasher loads weekly, and daily cooking. We were informed that a sewer back up occurred, and a small sump pump overflow had occurred. Most homes have accidents that are moisture related. From what we were told, these two small accidents did not appear to be significant.

image 13.101

The occupants of this home produce large amounts of moisture daily. It is our opinion, that even though the occupants of the home produce large amounts of moisture, this moisture solely, is not enough to have caused the significant amount of attic decking damage.

The attic has good ventilation, the basement walls do not leak, the crawl space does not leak, plumbing leaks were not seen today, and a dehumidifier was used in the basement. These were all signs of moisture and humidity control.

We were informed that:
- A new high efficient furnace was installed two years ago.
- The furnace company that installed this new furnace, repaired the old non-functional humidifier. We were informed that this humidifier had not operated for nine years, until the repair that occurred roughly two years ago.
- The furnace personnel turned on the humidifier and left.
- The furnace personnel did not inform the homeowners that they could not let the humidifier run continually in a tight home.
- The home has newer vinyl windows.

image 13.102

EXECUTIVE SUMMARY

During our inspection, the humidifier was running. This unit produced humidity every time the furnace fan turned on. It is possible, that this unit operated during other seasons as well. This home was tight and could not handle humidity this home was producing. The home produces so much moisture that the moisture condensates on all cold surfaces that are below their respective dew points. This was why the newer cold vinyl windows had mold and excessive dust accumulation. This was why fungal reservoirs exist in the attic, in the closet and on cold walls. Moisture was also leaving the home and condensating on the inside of the aluminum siding. Small icicles were seen on the exterior aluminum siding and in the small weep holes. It was also probable, that with two years of a constant running humidifier, the probability of interstitial fungal activity may have occurred.

The mold found in the second floor bathroom was being caused by many showers. The reason fungal activity was abundant in this bathroom was that the attic had significant mold spores. The bathroom wall got wet from condensation and mold spores attached and amplified.

Indoor humidity control should be the primary means to limit moisture accumulation in the attic, closest and cold walls. This home was built in a colder climate region and adequate attic ventilation should not have been the only safeguard to control moisture. The attic ventilation did help control heat during summer months and ice dam formation in the winter months.

SECTION FOURTEEN

Site Case Studies

The following is a collection of abreviated case studies designed to give basic site overviews and conclusion on some typical and not-so-typical microbial contamination.

Event

Water in the ducts under slab.

image 14.3

Site Observation

The exterior windows were badly condensating. The fogged windows were all condensating on the *interior* and not on the exterior. (Image 14.3)

Conclusion

image 14.1

You should always check first for CO or gas fired system problems. Water vapor is a major byproduct of combustion an could easily be the culprit for the elevated condensation as observed. In this case no problem existed with gas or fossil fuel systems. On slab homes, you must consider the duct work condition. Ductwork under slabs is not desirable unless it is perfect. Many systems detach, settle and/or pull apart. You must look in every floor register. Water in the ductwork is a serious problem. Check all rooms and all ductwork to see how extensive this condition may be. (Image 14.1).

image 14.4

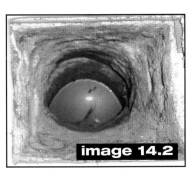

image 14.2

You do not need any fancy equipment to take photos, as most digital cameras fit in ducts. Image 14.2 shows a duct after many years of being flooded. It also shows contamination and fungal reservoirs. If you look at the ductwork you will see that the clay pipe used was not sealed at each joint (see image 14.4 & 14.5), therefore, water can enter at all joints. This water is evaporating in the home causing the windows to condensate on the interior. This condition has also caused the entire attic to become black mold covered. Mold is also amplifying behind the exterior walls. This home is in serious trouble.

image 14.5

Event

Ducts under the slab.

Site Observation

The gutters were leaking during a snow melt. A young couple just bought this home. On the day they moved in, they smelled gas and had it turned off for three days. Then the horror began.

Conclusion

The house became cold to about 38 degrees F. The gas leak was fixed and the gas was turned on. The home heated up to 68 degrees F. The siding started to drip water. The water was coming from behind the siding.

Rust stains on the exterior siding indicated that this was not the first time the house leaked from the inside out. It was literally raining in the attic. You needed an umbrella.

image 14.7

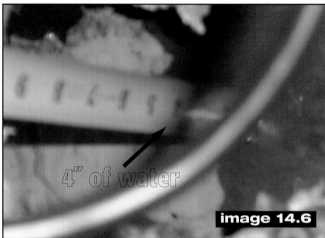
4" of water
image 14.6

image 14.8

The under slab ductwork had four inches of water. The furnace was causing the duct water to evaporate and causing high humidity and dew points to form throughout the dwelling. Water was condensing in the walls, on the walls, and in the attic.

Within ten days, the entire home was filled with mold. Mold was on all walls, in all walls, on all household belongings, in the attic, and under all carpets.

image 14.9

Event

Cross-contamination of the furnace discharge into the drainpipe in the floor below the washer. No mold, but this condition contributed to the client's illness.

Site Condition

This client was getting sick in her home. She thought she had mold problems. The home did in fact have some mold conditions from past occurrences and some leaking foundation walls. The furnace was reviewed and visually analyzed. The drain discharge from the AC and humidifier and the high efficient furnace was a hose type pipe. We followed it to the sink drain and discovered a major problem.

Conclusion

The discharge pipe from the furnace was submerged eight inches into the sanitary floor drain. A proper installation of condensate discharge would include an air gap between the end of disharge pipe and drain reservoir. This condition was allowing sewer fumes, bacteria, mold, and other toxic particles to enter into this discharge pipe. These contaminants then traveled through this hose into the furnace. Once in the furnace, the blower forced air over the drain pan, picking up contaminates and discharging them into the indoor air. This was a serious problem that has been known to kill people.

You must look at all drains, storm and discharge, and water treatment systems for cross-contamination conditions. You may be testing for mold in a home that actually has a bacteria problem.

image 14.10

Conclusion

This condition of mold amplification is occurring in the attic and is caused by hoarfrost. All homes produce humidity from many different sources. This humidity travels into the cooler attic space. It condenses and turns to frost on the attic sheathing usually starting on the northern exposure. The sun comes out and melts this frost. This moisture is absorbed into the wood sheathing and causes saturation. Mold spores attach themselves to this desirable medium and proliferate. This condition is further amplified by poor attic ventilation.

Adding more ventilation to this attic location is necessary. The humidifier on the furnace should also be monitored. Most people with humidifiers on furnaces leave them on all winter. This is a poor and dangerous practice. It increases the humidity in the home, which is transferred throughout all of the living spaces. At the very least, exhaust fans with humidistat controls (engaging the fan when either temperature *or* humidity levels become unfavorable) are an improvement.

image 14.11

image 14.12

Visible proof of poor attic ventilation in an ultra-humidified home

Event

Plumbing leaks.

Site Condition

This home was in foreclosure. The heat was off and the water was on during winter. The pipes froze and burst. The pipes leaked for one week. The house was empty for four months.

Conclusion

Vacant Building Syndrome (VBS) occurred. VBS is when an uncontrolled event occurs in an unoccupied building. In this case the entire interior of the building reached its saturation point. Humidity levels were extreme soon after saturation and stayed extreme for a long period of time.

Image 14.13:   Mushroom on carpet in the living room, it resembled a human ear.
Image 14.14:   Green mold in kitchen cupboard.
Image 14.15:   This is an ivy type fungi formation in the kitchen spice cabinet.
Image 14.16:   The fan wilted from the humidity.
Image 14.17:   Mushrooms are growing on the dining room ceiling.
Image 14.18:   Close-up of image of 6.17.
Image 14.19:   This is just one more room of all rooms that had visual mold.

This home is ruined and cannot be repaired economically.

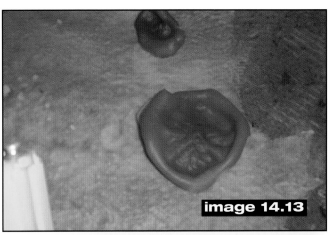

image 14.13

image 14.14

image 14.15

image 14.16

image 14.17

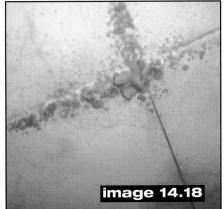

image 14.18

image 14.19

Event

Fungi is in the individual heating and cooling units.

Site Condition

This school had indoor air complaints and employees blamed it on out-gassing of the new carpets. The school system retained all types of experts to test the carpets.

It was obvious what the real problem was. Each office had its own air handler unit.

Conclusion

When you take the cover off, you see a new filter (Image 14.20). Great, but look at the condensation pan above this filter (Image 14.21). This is a possible reservoir for fungi and bacteria. This is a reservoir for a witch's brew. The fan blows over this area and aerosolizes the contaminants.

What is even more ironic is that these air handling unit discharge pipes were buried in mulch. *Mulch = Mold*. (Image 14.24).

Not only was the drain pan contaminated, the discharge pipe was cross-contaminating the air handling units. The employees were using air filters, air cleaners, fans, HEPA's, and plug-in fresheners. (Images 14.22 & 14.23).

image 14.20

image 14.21

image 14.22

FILTRATION IS NOT ALWAYS THE SOLUTION TO SANITATION.

image 14.23

image 14.24

Event

Mold caused by straw in new construction crawl space.

Site Condition

This was a million-dollar condominium being constructed during winter months in a northern state. The contractor used straw for winter protection so the concrete crawl slab would not freeze. This was a good idea because it kept the heat in the concrete during hydration (concrete reaction of getting hard).

Conclusion

The mistake was, they forgot about the straw and did not know enough about how long it takes for concrete hydration. It only takes 28 days for normal concrete to cure and not freeze. The contractor should have removed the straw after 28 days. It still would have been cold enough in the month of February that mold would generally not amplify in 20-32 degree weather.

When they finally went into the crawl space to clean up the straw, mold had covered virtually every timber. They could not understand what happened. Straw will naturally have mold spores that generally are not active during dry periods. Now, couple straw, mold spores, moisture, dark areas and you have the optimal combination and habitat for prolific fungi amplification.

This entire condominium was infected with mold fungal reservoirs.

image 14.25

image 14.26

image 14.27

Event

Contaminating agents that walk on eight legs.

Site Condition

Some think that the worst contaminants are usually molds, bacteria, and yeasts. One of the worst causes of contamination is mites. Mites are small relatives of spiders and ticks that often feed on fungi. They crawl from one source of mold to another.

Conclusion

Mites are quite small, sometimes less than $1/10$ mm long, and can come in a number of colors. The ones that most commonly get into homes are white to cream-colored and move rather slowly. Their eggs, also white, resemble tiny, smooth footballs scattered over the colony surface. All mites have eight legs, are usually covered with scattered bristles, and are often covered with spores.

Having dust mites doesn't mean that your home isn't clean. In most areas of the world, dust mites are in every house, no matter how clean. There is no practical way to completely rid your home of dust mites, unless you live in Antarctica or in an extremely dry climate. But keeping your home as dust free as possible can greatly lessen a dust mite allergy.

The fecal waste products of dust mites, not the dust mites themselves, are what cause allergic reactions. Dust mite fecal waste contains a protein that causes an allergic reaction for many people. A single dust mite can produce as much as 200 times its body weight in fecal waste. Even after dust mites die they leave their fecal waste behind, which continues to cause allergic reactions.

Studies show that more dust mites live in the bedroom than anywhere in the home. It is extremely important to wash the sheets, pillowcases and blankets in water temperatures of at least 130 degrees F.

The fecal matter of dust mites that live in your pillow and feed off your flakes of dead skin has a major impact on allergic reactions. An average human adult can shed up to 1.5 grams of skin a day – that's dinner for about 1 million dust mites.

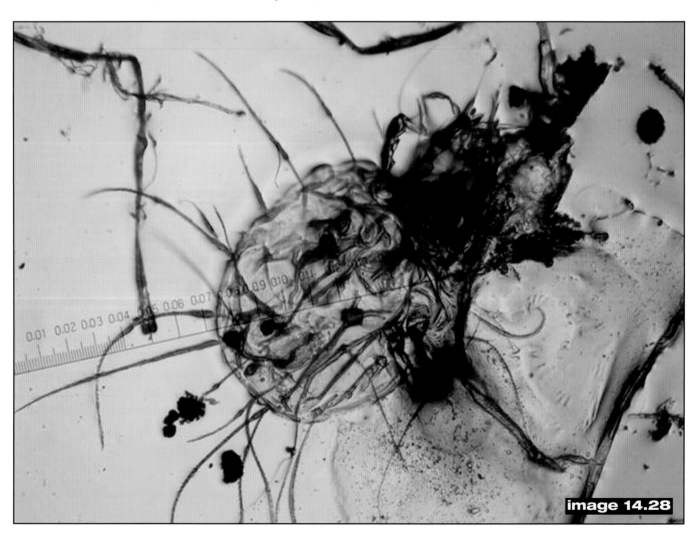

image 14.28

Event

Flooded crawl spaces

Site Condition

This home had three crawl spaces. This crawl space was hidden by nailed-up pegboard. Once removed, the entire area was seen and was flooded from poor exterior drainage and a failing drain tile system. It was very humid and the insulation was falling. Timber above this crawl space where water was ponding was also deteriorated. The plywood was rotted, delaminated, and had microbial amplification.

Moisture was high in this home and caused typical mold reservoirs. Mold behind the vinyl wallpaper, on drywall and on other locations was observed.

image 14.29

Conclusion

Moisture was so significant that it started to condensate in the attic and cause attic fungal activity. When we walked into this home, we saw air fresheners all over. These devices can make you sick without the mold.

image 14.30

image 14.31

image 14.32

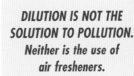

DILUTION IS NOT THE SOLUTION TO POLLUTION.
Neither is the use of air fresheners.

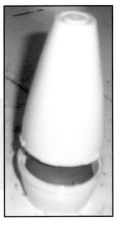

Event

Furniture covered with mold.

Site Observaion

These chairs were stored in a barn for a long period of time. If you look closely, the mold on these chairs resembles dust.

Conclusion

Mold does not have to look like big black spots. This is sometimes referred to by the general public as mildew. The in-style lovely light blue leather couch is also a good mold medium. It is not a good idea to leave any textiles, furniture, or cellulose products in areas that will naturally have high humidity. Barns are for horses, not for old antique collectible furniture. Next time you are garage "sailing", see if the store has a musty odor. It is probably the mold in the furniture they bought from someone who had a barn.

Plug in an ultra-violet light, the one kids use in their rooms for glow-in-the-dark posters. Put the light next to this powdery mildew, mold or dust. Many times, if it glows, it is surely mold. You can also check your wood paneling in the basement this way. Mold can amplify so thin, that is not seen by the naked eye in darker rooms. As consultants we never really tried this mold testing method, but we did see it being used as quality control for inspecting fungal spots on circuit boards in electronics factories during one of our investigations.

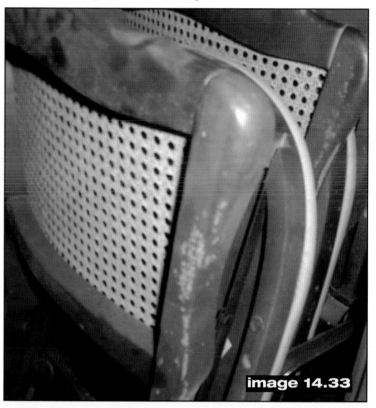

image 14.33

image 14.34

Event

Mold on the furniture.

Site Condition

Always look at furniture in the home for mold. Mold is saprophytic and finds mediums that have nutrients, i.e., any cellulose material. If you see mold on furniture, you probably have a microbial condition occurring that is water related. Look behind wood dressers. Image 14.35 is the back of a dresser that is against a basement wall. This old home had occupants that never used a dehumidifier. They never used the basement either, otherwise, they would have noticed a problem occurring. Always look under the cushions of leather or fabric furniture. Image 14.35a is a couch with its cushions lifted that is located in this same room as the upper dresser.

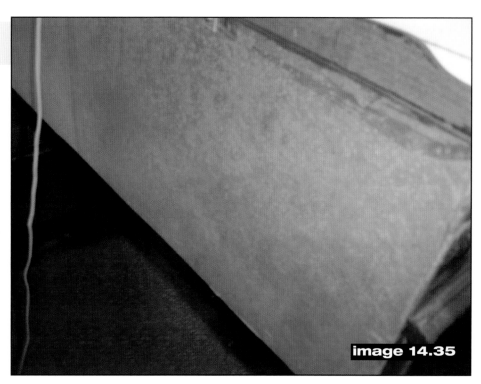

image 14.35

Conclusion

When mold is found on furniture, it will typically outgas MVOC's (Microbial Volatile Organic Compounds) and produce a musty odor. Volatile here means vaporous, as in flammable.

Walk very briskly in the front yard of a home and breath through you nose. This will cleanse your upper respiratory tract. Then walk in the front door and immediately breathe through your nose. If you smell musty odors, you have mold, and you need to start looking for reservoirs. Generally, if musty odors are faint, within minutes you will get used to it and no longer smell the musty odor. Powdery mildew is the cause of the VOC activity.

image 14.35a

Event

Mold found behind paint on the exterior wall.

Site Condition

Mold was suspected on the interior side of the exterior walls of the building. Mold was found at other locations that were wall-papered in other rooms. Mold spores were found in the air using non-viable testing. It was probable, that since mold existed behind wallpaper in other rooms, it would exist behind paint. When a small section of wall was chipped away, black mold was encountered. This mold was found to contain *Stachybotrys chartum*[1] from laboratory analysis.

Conclusion

When you apply psychrometrics to mold investigations you can predict certain outcomes. This unit has high humidity at low temperatures. When rooms are shut down for the winter the temperatures are lowered. Lower air temperatures hold less moisture. Furthermore, the outside walls are much colder and dew point is the outcome. The dew point condensed behind the paint on the cellulose face of the drywall. *Stachybotrys chartum* is a slimy looking mold that loves cellulose mediums. If you find mold behind wallpaper in one room and you have other rooms that have no wallpaper, you should check and make sure that the exterior wall has no visible mold. The exterior walls tend to be colder and dew points can form in the wall cavity or behind finished surfaces and cove base. See image 14.38.

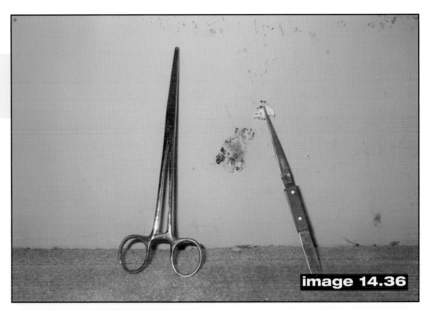

image 14.36

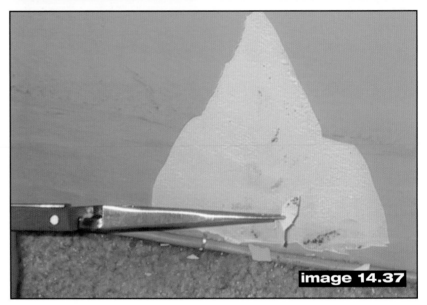

image 14.37

image 14.38

[1] *This means paper loving.*

Event

Mold amplification behind the vinyl wallpaper in a high rise condominium unit on the tenth floor.

Site Observation

Most of the exterior walls in this unit had vinyl wallpaper installed. It was determined that mold existed on most perimeter walls that had this vinyl wallpaper.

Moisture is coming from the interior of this unit. The moisture that is causing this mold is coming from the exterior in the humid summer months. The exterior air is warm with high humidity. This particular occupant liked the conditioned air in her home very cool. The AC was set to 72° F.

image 14.39

Conclusion

Using psychrometric charts, if it rained on a summer day and the temperature on the exterior was 80° F with a humidity of 80%, the dew point would be 76° F.

This unit's bathroom fan was always on. This fan would depressurize the entire unit and suck warm and moist air into the unit from the exterior. You only need 76° for dew point (condensation) with this example. This condominium unit had vinyl wallpaper that was not permeable. The moisture would condense behind the wallpaper and fungi would live off of the wall paper nutrients. This also is a common problem with hotels and high rise buildings.

image 14.40

Event

EIF's systems allow mold amplification behind them.

(EIFS / Stucco / Synthetic Stucco / Exterior Cladding are some of the names of this type of exterior product.)

Site Observation

This was a site that was hit by a tornado. The tornado opened up the wall of this 500K+ condominium. These executive and exclusive condominiums were roughly ten years old. When we inspected the superstructure behind the exterior cladding we found deterioration to the components from many years of moisture activity.

CONCLUSION

Many of these early exterior type cladding installations have received national publicity. Many class action lawsuits are still pending. These systems fail, due to poor design, poor installation, and poor maintenance. Depressurization, dew points, and wind effects are also contributors to this type of deterioration. All exterior siding systems, such as these, require full moisture surveys. Testing can be done with infrared or with moisture meters. Interstitial mold is probable with many of these older systems. Most people that live in these homes do not know that they have problems within their walls.

image 14.41

image 14.42

image 14.43

Event

Ice dams and the chimney system.

Site Observation

The roof had problems with ice dams. This was the north side of the dwelling. The insulation was disturbed in the center of the attic. On certain days, the snow would melt at the upper roof portion, directly over the area that had disturbed insulation. The heat would rise quicker here and melt the roof snow. The water would run down the roof shingles. On the north side, also a shade area, no soffit vents existed and the insulation was stuffed into the overhang. There is no cricket behind the chimney (a cricket is a small extension of the roofline which is located at the junction of the roof and the chimney that redirects run off water from the roof around the chimney, instead of the water rushing down the roof and stressing the flashing at the base of the chimney head-on). It is inevitable that ice would form there. Ice formed, and when it melted, it would leak indoors and into the interstitial space.

Conclusion

This condition continues and causes indoor microbial contamination. The solution to this condition is to add more insulation in the attic area. Secondly, one can install soffit vents and ridge vents to allow for air movement. Thirdly, a cricket can be added to the back of the chimney. The clients also installed heat cables on the roofing membrane for back up. This condition of wall mold was also corrected. The insurance company paid for all remediation and repair. Many of today's policies cover water damage but do not cover mold.

image 14.44

image 14.45

Event

Water leaking into the crawl space.

Site Observation

The foundation walls were leaking at the lower block. A history of wet and dry puddle marks is seen throughout this entire crawl space location.

Sometimes when looking for mold you find water. Water generally equals mold. In the lower digital image, you will see water marks at the masonry joints. This means that the hollow block is filled with water. This is a problem that will lead to microbial contamination. This block is causing high humidity during foundation evaporation. High humidity will cause dew points and condensation. Air testing for fungi would probably give positive results.

Conclusion

This crawl space needs to be waterproofed and purged of microbial contamination. This area needs to be waterproofed prior to any microbial abatement. The high humidity condition will spread to the upper home and could cause condensation in the attic. The attic had mold growth on the north side. When you have crawlspace moisture infiltration, you must always check all attic locations for condensation conditions.

image 14.46

image 14.47

Event

Moisture meter test conducted because a window is defective and interstitial moisture migration is suspected.

Site Observation

The owner of this home was concerned with moisture stains in his living room under several of the windows. Be very careful with windows manufactured between 1987 and 1993. Several name brand windows have been made with defective wood preservatives. Ten years later, the windows dry rot and leak (Serpula). Most of the homes with these defective windows are upper middle income homes. Check the Internet for the name brands and for the class action lawsuit information. We find that the owners of these types of windows, repair the rot with bondo or wood filler and repaint them. This practice of concealment is widespread throughout the country.

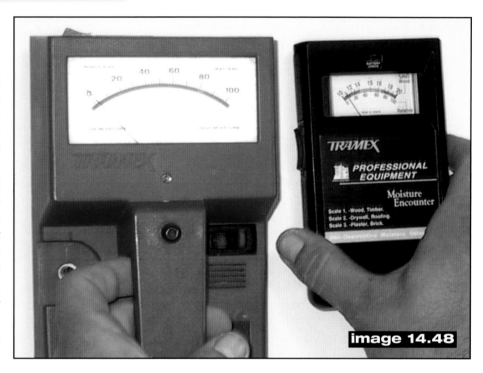

image 14.48

Conclusion

Many times moisture cannot be seen and specialized equipment is needed. In the upper digital image (14.48), a test was done above the window where leaking was not suspected. The readings were zero and dry. In the lower digital image (14.49), the moisture readings were taken below the defective windows. The readings showed that moisture was present. This is a major problem due to the potential of interstitial moisture and fungal activity within the wall system. The use of moisture meters is critical in locating the source of water. Remember that water is necessary for the amplification of fungal reservoirs. We found that the more sensitive the moisture meters the higher the readings.

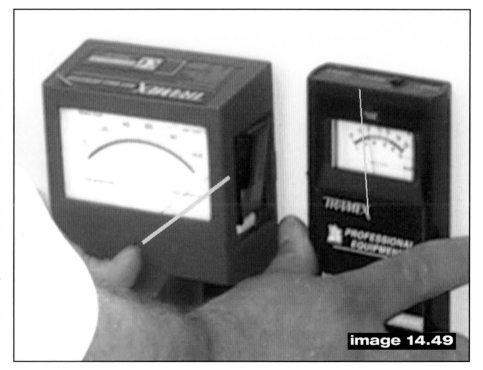

image 14.49

Water from a discharge pipe leaking into a crawlspace.

Site Observation

An unusual condition was occurring in the crawl space. Water was draining from the AC and humidifier units from the floor above.

All areas of the home must be inspected. Discharge drains should leave a minimum of one inch between line and reservoir to provide an air gap. This is necessary to prevent cross contamination and potential microbial growth in the heating system. This installation is improper, due to dripping condensation running off the drain grate. The floor was full of dust, and mold amplification was the result. Water reservoirs that exist under a home in crawl spaces are not desirable and potentially can contaminate the entire dwelling (See Image 14.50).

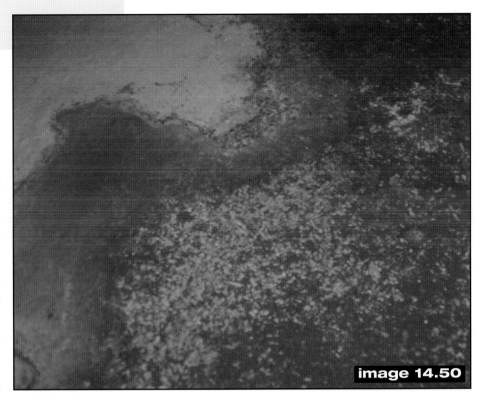

image 14.50

Do not mistake mold for bacteria. If Image 14.51 had the discharge pipe submerged into the floor drain liquid, bacteria could contaminate the entire heating system. Legionella is one such bacterium that can cause contamination of the entire heating system.

Conclusion

Dripping water is deflecting off of the drain cover. A combination of mold and bacteria has resulted. This discharge pipe should have its length increased and the crawl slab purged of biogrowth. This condition is also adding excessive humidity to the crawl space environment from evaporation.

image 14.51

Event

Above the drop ceiling, the joists and sheathing both have visual mold amplification.

Site Observation

Significant mold is found amplifying on the joist and sparse mold is seen amplifying on the plywood sheathing. When you first see this condition, you need to determine how this could have occurred. If mold were just on the joist, then the mold could have been brought in on the wood during construction. The plywood sheathing also had mold and the first assumption is still possible. By both areas having mold, it is highly probable that an event or events occurred. You should look for evidence of past moisture problems that would lead to this mold condition.

image 14.52

Conclusion

After interviewing the client, we found that the dwelling had a series of major storm water backups due to city sewer conditions. The city replaced the underground lines, and the backups have ceased. The problem of mold still exists even after the repair. The ceiling tile acted as a vapor barrier. Moisture was trapped in the cavity created by the ceiling tile and the subfloor. Mold was found consistently on 90 percent of the joists and sheathing that were reviewed.

image 14.53

Event

Joist conditions found under a restaurant kitchen in a vintage building.

Site Condition

The restaurant was temporarily closed down due to unsanitary conditions. The city health inspector told the owners they had to clean up the kitchen walls and floors. The white material you see is mold growing on what appears to be either grease from the kitchen or some kind of kitchen leakage. Whatever this sticky medium is, mold seems to be amplifying on it. Mold is saprophytic and opportunistic. Whatever this is, mold is using it as a host. Mold will attach and amplify on mediums that serve as nutrients. This is usually cellulose or other fungi. This leaking restaurant substance is a good nutrient. The above health official never went to the basement to make this joist observation.

image 14.54

Conclusion

The entire restaurant's walls were made of inexpensive, thin paneling. It was decided to remove this old paneling. Wood cellulose products are not desirable for areas that are subject to water, food or food-laden moisture. We never actually tested this white stuff because the owners had a very limited budget for the mold investigation. After they cleaned up the first floor, we were asked to perform a post-abatement clearance. We declined to perform the test, due to the visual presence of mold still existing in the basement.

image 14.55

Event

The subfloor had deteriorated under the bathroom.

Site Observation

The subfloor had partially deteriorated under the first floor bathroom. In Image 14.57, one can see the new OSB sheathing that was replaced as a result of a history of leaking. Always look under the bathroom locations when areas are accessible. All bathrooms will leak at some point in time. When leaks occur below second floor bathrooms, the ceiling generally is stained and repairs are done rather quickly. When the first floor bathroom leaks, many homeowners let them leak for long periods of time. This can be due to slab, crawl, or an isolated basement. In the lower portion, the entire area under the toilet was replaced due to a toilet seal leak. It leaked for a long time because a large portion of the floor had to be replaced. If leaks are caught and repaired in the first 48 hours, mold will probably not form reservoirs.

image 14.56

Conclusion

The jackleg of a repairman did not remove enough of the deterioration from past bathroom leaks. From Image 14.57, you can still see wood rot and mold.

image 14.57

Event

Mold in new home found on joists and the structural wood beams.

Site Condition

Mold was found on numerous basement joists and numerous basement wood structural beams. Mold was not found on OSB sheathing. This mold was brought in during the home construction. The construction site soil also contains thousands of spores. The mold was found on mostly larger timbers. When, and if, the homeowner complains, the builder will say that this mold is dead and not growing. He is probably correct, as long as the humidity in the home does not go over 50 percent. The other problem is that this mold is also on the joists on the second and attic floors that are usually concealed from view. If interstitial moisture occurs, amplification will begin. Just because the mold is not amplifying today, does not mean it will not amplify in the future. Someday, this home will be sold to a new prospective buyer and a home inspector will once again identify the mold condition.

image 14.58

Conclusion

The mold tested at several isolated locations was found to be *Penicillium*, *Aspergillus*, and *Cladosporium*, which is the most common mold of all. These types of molds can cause discomfort in sensitized individuals. Mold spores are allergenic, regardless if alive or dead. Simply walking on the first floor will cause vibrations that will release mold spores into the basement airspace.

image 14.59

Event

This is an older home that has mold on the joists in the basement.

Site Observation

Most of the basement joists have mold. The attic rafters that are the same dimension 2 X 10's have some slight visual mold reservoirs. The mold that you see is significant. When you look at the joists, always look at the sheathing. In this case, the sheathing is OSB, and no mold existed. The same lumber in the attic has some sparse mold. The conclusion is that the builder built the home with mold on the wood. The reason the basement mold is more significant is that the builder also did not implement moisture controls during the construction phase. Basements stay wet the entire time the home is under construction. The sparse mold is already on the wood from the lumberyard and can amplify in the wet basement during construction. Next time you see a home under construction, go to the basement. You will probably find signs of past leakage activity, standing water or even flooding.

image 14.60

Conclusion

The particular mold found was *Penicillium* and *Aspergillus*. The basement humidity was only 41 percent and mold reservoirs were not amplifying. The basement had no musty odors. All joists must be professionally sanded and HEPA vacuumed. Simply painting over this mold is not the desired abatement method. This type of condition does not diminish or hamper the structural integrity of the wood. Light sanding with HEPA vacuuming should remove the mold. Work should be done under negative pressure and containment.

image 14.61

Event

Mold on basement joists of new home.

Site Observation

Mold was seen on several basement joists. The OSB board did not have any mold contamination. Be careful with new home construction. In the northern states, many homes are being built with moldy wood. This joist was most probably on the bottom of the delivered woodpile. Carpenters do not look for mold on wood. New homebuyers should inspect the home for mold during their walk-through inspection. New homebuyers never check for mold on the wood, until they see it in the news or on television. If possible, the new homebuyer should inspect the wood shell prior to interior installations.

Many super-lumberyards will bid on large lumber lots. They usually never see what they buy until the lumber is delivered. It costs too much money to send moldy components back to the distributors. They shuffle the wood and sell it to the public. Builders do not go to the lumberyards to inspect the wood prior to ordering. Builders do not de-humidify the home during the construction phase. The entire building process from the beginning does not incorporate a mold prevention factor. Recently, all over the country, builders and lumberyards are being brought to litigation due to mold on wood. A time will come when builders become more cognizant of mold on their construction sites. Until that time, it should be the responsibility of the new homebuyer to identify the problem before they purchase.

Conclusion

The builder was notified about this problem from the prospective homebuyer. The builder did nothing about this issue. The prospective homebuyer walked from the deal and did not purchase the home. It is important that the inspector alerts the client to the potential of microbial situations.

image 14.62

Event

Roof repairs covered an already moisture saturated primary roof system.

Site Condition

The ceiling has active moisture stains. These stains were determined to be active using several different moisture gauges. A hole was punched into the ceiling for aggressive observation . Moisture was found to be active within the interstitial ceiling space.

If you do not have a moisture gauge to help in your evaluation, you should consider using everyday household items. Take a section of plastic wrap and tape it firmly to the ceiling on all four sides. Come back the next day. If water is beading behind the plastic, then moisture is trapped in the interstitial space. If water is beading on the exterior surface, then the humidity in the room is excessive.

image 14.63

Conclusion

Image 14.64 is a close-up of Image 14.63. The water is beading on the roof's underside. This condition was not a roof leak. The water dripping on the interior of this area was actually interior house moisture that was trapped and condensation on the cold roof sheathing. The investigators found the slab room had underground ducts that were flooded and full of water. The heating system caused evaporation of the moisture, which moved to the attic interstitial space through vapor diffusion.

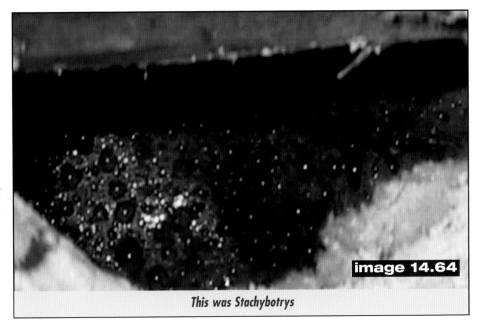

image 14.64

This was Stachybotrys

Event

Mold growth on interior hotel walls made after the vinyl wallpaper is removed.

Site Condition

This was a multi-story hotel that was being occupied by guests on the lower five floors. While the upper floors were under construction these floors were contaminated with mold. This is a major problem which goes unnoticed by the public. Many of the hotels we stay in are full of mold. The design of these buildings is conducted in a manner that would naturally produce mold. These buildings have poor interstitial exoskeleton design that has improper engineering. The owners install vinyl wallpaper on the interior walls that serves as a vapor barrier. The moisture gets trapped behind the wallpaper and amplifies on the nutrients of the wallpaper paste. You can smell a musty odor. Do you ever wake up in the morning in a hotel room with a congested feeling?

Conclusion

This hotel was severely contaminated. It was even more contaminated due to the contractors renovating and improperly abating the mold. The areas were not under negative pressure and were not separated by containment from the other occupied building floors. The elevators were for the guests as well as the construction workers. Mold spores were allowed to travel down elevator shafts and contaminate the lower units. We got on and off on the third floor which was completely remodeled. Guests were all over. Every time the elevator door opened you smelled a musty odor. These odors are microbial volatile organic compounds or MVOC's. In this instance, the elevator and shaft helped to further contaminate this site.

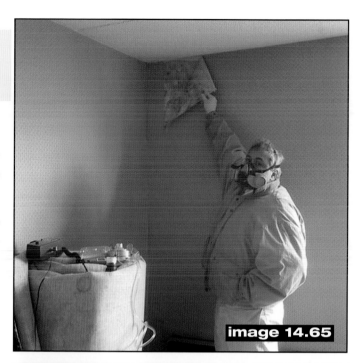

image 14.65

image 14.66

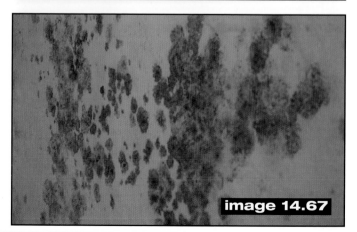

image 14.67

Event

Mold is amplifying on the leather of this jacket in the closet.

image 14.68

Site Condition

There was a water leak above this closet. The coat was found in the far end of the closet. The wall also had some mold on the surface. We pulled this leather jacket out to have it tested.

You may need to refer to the IICRC[1] Guidelines for the cleaning of storage and materials. You can get this information on the Internet. Check the contents of the home for suspect mold contamination. Always look in closets that have restricted air movement or are unconditioned spaces. The closets are generally cooler areas. The outer walls of these closets form dew points quicker than other walls within the dwelling.

Conclusion

This home had a roof leak that was repaired. The roof leak had lasted for some time. The leak did cause mold conditions and some deterioration. Several months after cleaning and roof repair, the owners of the dwelling noticed mold reservoirs on closet walls and on the contents in closets. The roofer installed an attic fan that caused the home to depressurize. Every time the attic fan would turn on, moisture was being sucked out of the two crawl spaces. This moisture was not being controlled by dehumidification. The moisture traveled throughout the home via vapor diffusion. The colder closet walls allowed dew point. This provides an optimal environment for mold amplification. Leather is a good medium for saprophytic mold reservoirs. The interim solution to the depressurization was to disconnect the attic fan and install a basement and crawl dehumidifier. The long-term repairs are to waterproof the crawl locations and diminish the potential from moisture diffusion. Dehumidifiers should be used for interim controls only. They should not be the remedies for moisture problems.

image 14.69

This couch is leather and is totally covered with colonies. It was located in another highly contaminated dwelling.

---

[1] IICRIC is a suggested specifiecation on cleaning fungal contamination.

Event

Investigator is looking for mold behind the baseboard.

image 14.70

Site Observation

This home is vacant. The home did not have significant mold reservoirs. The home was suspected to have mold due to a disclosure of a past plumbing leak. The plumbing leak and home were repaired by a mold abatement firm. The inspectors visited this site and conducted an investigation.

Laymen or non-professional people forget to look for mold behind the baseboard for contamination. This is a condition that exists in homes that have past moisture events. They can also promulgate from negative pressure, condensation, and wet carpet cleaning.

Conclusion

The abatement contractor did a poor job of mold removal. The mold was also found under the carpets and behind the wallpaper. The mold found behind the base board was not caused by the initial plumbing leak itself. The plumbing leaks caused higher humidity in the dwelling. The moisture is trapped between the wood baseboard and vinyl wallpaper. The vinyl wallpaper acted liked a vapor barrier. The mold found nutrients on the wall behind the baseboard.

image 14.71

Event

A new home with steps which have mold growth on one side only.

Site Observation

Mold is on the new steps. The walls were just painted and the carpet installers were scheduled to come in. Mold is on the kick plate and on the tread. It was odd that mold was not seen on the underside of the steps. During new construction the basement is always damp or humid. The longer it takes to build a home, the longer the basement stays wet. We have yet to see a builder use a dehumidifier in a basement during construction. The sub-contractors go up and down these steps with their boots on. The sub-contractors go out to their tool trucks and back into the home all day. They walk through the mud, the wet grass, and the wet basement floor. Hygiene is ignored during construction.

image 14.72

Conclusion

This is an interesting case. If the wood initially had mold brought in, we would see it also under the steps or on the backside of the steps. The mold is at locations where worker's boots would have hit. The boots were contaminated from exterior and interior mold sources. The boots were also getting wet from interior and exterior sources. Our conclusion is that the work boots of construction workers pick up mold spores. The builder claims that the marks are from the soles of the boots. Laboratory analysis indicates *Cladosporium*. Psychrometrics helps conclude that the moisture and humidity levels during the construction stage are optimal for microbial amplification.

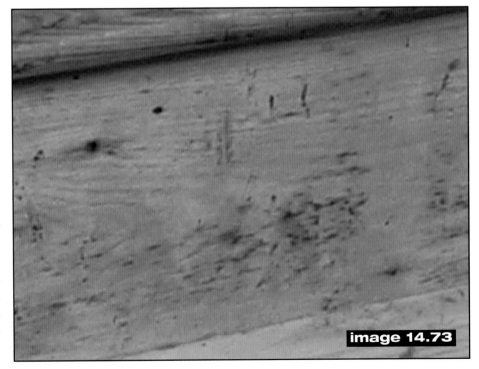

image 14.73

Site Observation

In the upper digital image (14.74), one can see the mold on the wallpaper and behind the drywall after a section was cut out. In the lower photo (14.75), one can see the surface mold on the painted drywall. Mold will grow on basement finished and non-finished walls. Basements are humid, especially in vintage homes. The older homes have old sluggish drain tile systems. Older homes can have poor grading and plugged gutters. Some moisture will enter into the basement due to these conditions. The high humidity will cause dew points to form and mold amplification is the result. You do not know if mold exists behind the wall, unless you use sophisticated equipment, i.e , a borescope. Generally, you need to cut out suspect areas for viewing. Never assume that if mold exists on the surface that none exists on the backside.

image 14.74

Conclusion

In Image 14.74, the mold was caused by high humidity in the basement. The reason why mold was suspect behind the dry wall was because this basement was negatively pressurized.

The dryer was sucking air out of the basement. A window exhaust fan was operating with a closed basement door. Moisture is being pulled in from the exterior basement walls. Moisture is trapped within the interstitial wall cavity. The insulation vapor barrier was not properly installed and it allowed moisture to pass through. The condition causes a dew point to form behind the drywall. Mold contamination and amplification is the result.

image 14.75

Event

Mushroom is growing through the vinyl siding.

Site Observation

This home is only four years old. The home had vinyl siding with no house wrap. The mushroom is not growing on the vinyl siding. The mushroom is growing through the siding cracks. Behind the siding is OSB sheathing. The mushroom is attached to the OSB.

Conclusion

The top of this chimney is not properly flashed. Water is leaking behind the vinyl siding. This chimney is not house-wrapped. It had been leaking for four years. If this home had house-wrap underneath the vinyl siding, this condition may not have occurred. House-wrap also can serve as a defense against water that migrates behind the vinyl siding. The chimney flashing was critical to this condition. The entire chimney vinyl has to be removed and all wet and damaged sheathing needs to be replaced. It is highly probable that this chimney also has intestinal mold. Water can easily enter the inner wall cavity at OSB splices.

image 14.76

image 14.77

Event

A closer look at mushrooms. Mushrooms that are growing on a log in the salmon stream are okay. Mushrooms that are growing in your home are not okay.

Site Condition

The mushroom was found growing in Image 14.78 was in a fine home that was only two years old. The owners never knew this condition existed because this home had a living room which was rarely used. The moisture content of the interior window wood was over 20%. The window was found to be defective due to a seal condition. This window had a slow leak every time it rained. The wood window faced the southwest and had plenty of light. The wood window served as a medium for the mushrooms just like the salmon stream log in Image 14.79.

Conclusion

If the wind were blowing from the southwest direction during rainfall, the window would leak. Additionally, the wood window faced the southwest and had plenty of light. Mushrooms can make many people sick, especially when they break apart. When you break up a mushroom, millions of spores are released. If a person that is immune-compromised or a person with allergies is exposed, serious health effects can occur.

Check the window components for mold amplification. Furniture had to be moved to access this window. It does not take a long period of time, under the right conditions, for the mushrooms to grow.

image 14.78

Mushrooms growing on the sash of a sliding window.

image 14.79

Mushrooms growing on a log at a Rochester, NY salmon stream.

Event

Mold colonization is on the walls and ceiling of the entire bathroom.

Site Observation

The entire bathroom is contaminated with black greenish mold. This unit was vacated only three weeks prior. The old tenant left the hot water fixture open. It ran constantly for three weeks. The unit was located on the north side on the second floor of a three-story, multi-unit apartment building.

VHS or Vacant Home Syndrome is a common problem when homes are left vacant with moisture conditions. Many times, utilities are left open or turned off when tenants vacate, get evicted, or get foreclosed on. The empty home no longer has controlled interior atmospheric conditions. Sump pumps fail, pipes freeze, roofs leak, basements have high humidity, dew points are occurring, and humidity is no longer controlled.

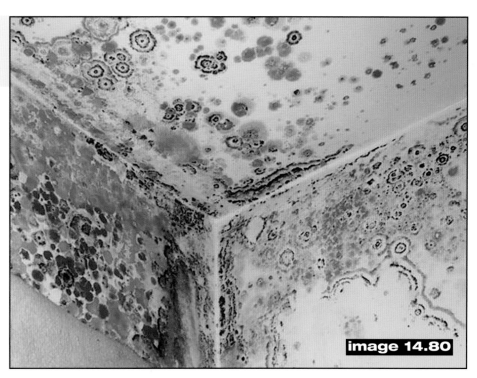

image 14.80

Conclusion

This unit was vacated with a slightly running sink faucet that went unnoticed. The dripping was slowly evaporating in the unit. The air was cold due to the utilities being turned off. The air at one point became saturated and a dew point was formed. The north unit was the colder location. Moisture condensation is the result. The wet walls were unnoticed and normal airborne spores attached. This dew point condition occurred on several occasions and mold reservoirs were formed. The entire unit, after a short period of time, was full of mold. This type of condition can almost be predicted with the use of psychrometric charts.

image 14.81

Event

Mold growth on the wood paneling near the washer-dryer area.

Site Observation

Many molds have a black color or tint. This is, many times, mistaken for the black mold that is on TV shows. *Stachybotrys* is what the general public calls "black mold." This example shows black mold to be a common household mold. One of the highest potential mold locations in all basements is the laundry area. Always check behind the washer and dryer. These areas have frequent temperature changes and mold-causing conditions. Water splashes against the wall from discharge hoses. Water backs-up at floor drains due to excessive lint and debris. Old washer hoses can, and do break—thereby flooding homes. One flood can easily cost over $10K.

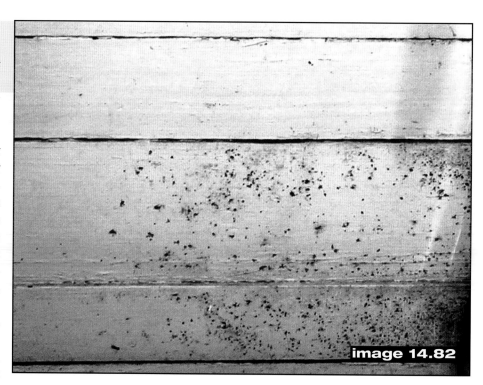

image 14.82

Conclusion

Walls that are located near laundry and utility areas should be cleaned more frequently. Mold spores can get on clothes and make immune compromised people ill. We recommended having this wood paneling removed. "When in doubt, rip it out" philosophy should be considered. The walls and paneling could be scrubbed with TSP and HEPA vacuumed. In vintage homes with basement moisture infiltration, wall paneling is not recommended. It will only serve as a host to annoying molds. Wet or moist basements should not be finished until the condition is repaired.

image 14.83

Event

Exterior door leaks with poor trim flashing and no threshold sealant.

Site Observation

There is fresh paint and caulk on the door trim. Rotted wood is found at both the top wood trim and the door base. This is a serious condition and many times is an overlooked problem. Dry rot is mold. Leaking doors also have high potential to have interstitial mold. As mentioned earlier, in the late 1980's and early 1990's, several window and door manufacturers used wood preservatives that failed.

Conclusion

The trim around this door is improperly installed and caulked. The irregular installation caused the trim to leak. It was leaking from the top, flowing or draining behind the trim to the door's base. When this door was removed, sparse mold was within the wall system. The insulation was wet and the R-value was lowered. The siding J-channel was also improperly cut and installed. Water is running down the siding and is not being deflected by the J-channel. The wood product is also defective and is very susceptible to rot when wet. These conditions are usually not covered by insurance companies. Water infiltration that helps foster a suitable microbial habitat can be found at the simplest of locations such as a trim joint.

image 14.85

image 14.85a

Corner has bondo and excessive caulk that still failed.

Event

New condominium that has a French door leak at the threshold.

Site Condition

The French door had leaks that were causing damage to the subfloor system. On a side note, the owners of this unit were getting sick. They thought they were getting sick from this leaking door that was causing mold to amplify. The mold growth at this location was sparse and minimal. You need to evaluate the entire environment. Our clients stated that they had been getting sick for the last four months. This just happened to be the entire winter of 2002. After asking some questions, we learned that these clients also purchased a ventless fireplace. We were also informed that the ventless fireplace was used daily while windows remained closed.

image 14.86

Conclusion

The photos depict common damage from leaking patio and French or sliding doors. This damage generally transfers to the band joists, subfloor, and sill in the basement. This problem generally costs homeowners several thousand dollars to correct. But this condition was not making our clients sick. We tested the air after running this vent- less fireplace for six hours. The home was so tight that minimal or virtually no air exchanges occurred. The oxygen supply was being depleted. We found that the CO_2 levels were over 1500 PPM. The exterior levels are generally 350-400 PPM. The recommended interior levels should be less than 700 PPM. The 1500 PPM was excessive and caused drowsiness and other ailments. The clients never became ill after they improved the fresh air ventilation.

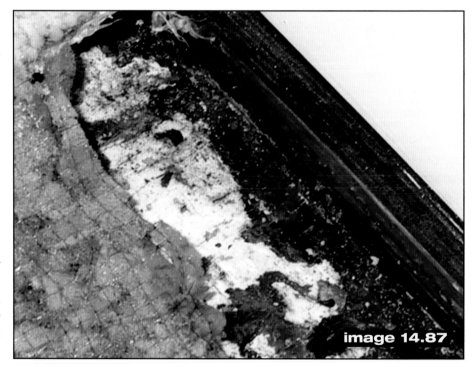

image 14.87

Event

Attic mold on the north gable wall.

Site Observation

Mold growth is found on the attic sheathing and on the gable end walls. The owners of this home did not know if this mold condition was actively amplifying. Investigators performed a time duration evaluation. This first inspection was conducted in the Fall. The second inspection was conducted in the Spring after Winter had passed.

Investigators knew that this mold was caused by winter condensation. Investigators were not sure if it was active, due to no odor and low relative humidity in the attic location during the summer inspection. Ten years ago, a new roof along with ridge venting was installed. It was possible that the mold was no longer amplifying. If you spend money removing this mold now, it may grow back later. You need to remove the cause of the moisture first.

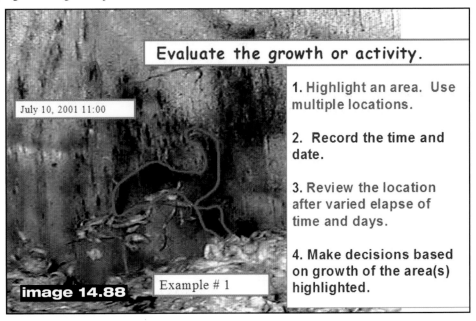

Evaluate the growth or activity.

July 10, 2001 11:00

1. Highlight an area. Use multiple locations.

2. Record the time and date.

3. Review the location after varied elapse of time and days.

4. Make decisions based on growth of the area(s) highlighted.

image 14.88   Example # 1

Conclusion

Mold amplification was determined to be active. Ventilation[1] and roofing conditions were found to be insufficient for this particular home. The humidifier was suspected. It was never turned off during furnace cycles. A heating expert determined that the humidifier was defective and always on when the furnace fan ran. This unit produced many grains of moisture per hour. These grains accumulated because the home was tight. The additional grains caused saturation of the air in the attic. This condition was more than the attic ventilation could handle. The result was condensation and mold. The humidifier was removed and the mold was abated.

image 14.89

---

[1] *Attic ventilation should be one square foot per each one hundred fifty square foot of attic floor space.*

Event

Sparse mold on the attic sheathing and components.

Site Observation

Always look into the attic. Most attic accesses are found in bedroom closets. You will fit in these access areas due to size access requirements from fire laws. Attic mold on sheathing will always start growing on the north side. It usually starts at the soffit and moves upward toward the ridge.

We find that many homes built in the 1970's through to the early 1990's have a potential for attic mold. This is because, in the 1970's building designs changed and the homes were made tighter. The split-level, ranch, colonial, and cathedral-designed homes were the most susceptible. The energy crisis that started around the mid 1970's had building designers who were more focused on saving energy than moisture elimination. Poor attic ventilation was the outcome. This was also a time when furnace installers had high-selling pitches for add-on humidifiers. Unfortunately, they were better salesmen than engineers. People with these units would turn them on and leave them on all winter. We find in sheathing attic mold conditions, poor ventilation and a continuous running furnace humidifier are the cause.

image 14.90

Conclusion

This condition of mold amplification that is occurring in the attic location is caused by hoarfrost. This humidity traveled into the cooler attic space. It condensates and turns into frost on the attic sheathing. When the temperature changed, and melted this frost, moisture was absorbed into the wood sheathing and caused saturation. Mold spores attached themselves to this desirable medium and proliferated. This mold was found to be an allergenic type called *Cladosporium*. *Cladosporium* is the most common mold found in the home and is usually always airborne in the exterior air. The *Cladosporium* spores find their way into attics through roof vents. They attach themselves to the sheathing and amplification begins. The attic may have several to many hoarfrost cycles per winter. By blocking the ventilation and restricting the flow of air in and out, a condition is created that may exacerbate the amplification of fungal activity.

image 14.91

View of blocked vent

image 14.92

This is an attic with sparse mold developing.
This attic had ridge vents with the soffit vents blocked.
For proper ventilation, ridge and soffit vents need to be functional.

Site Observation

The home was built in 1956. The exterior grading was level. The exterior had old, existing storm drain lines. The interior basement was 70% finished with knotty pine. The bottom base had moisture stains. The basement had a musty odor. Although this is considered sparse mold it can still be a problem. Many homes in this 1950's era had this type of paneling installed. It takes a long time for this material to show signs of rot. The mold types also vary and always need to be verified prior to renovation. You may have toxigenic mold behind the paneling. When non-professionals remove this paneling, they can release billions of air-borne spores. Be careful, when removing this material because the floor will be disturbed as well. These old floors are considered to have asbestos containing material or ACBMs.

image 14.93

Conclusion

The mold species found were allergenic and mycotoxic types. The moisture readings taken led us to believe that the basement drain tile was slow, sluggish, and leaking. The home had to be waterproofed. You must stop the water source prior to remediating mold. We were informed that the odor did not start until recently. This was odd due to the moisture stains being old and ongoing. Later it was discovered that just recently, a new efficient furnace was installed. This furnace no longer utilized the chimney for the discharge of effluent combustion gas. A plastic PVC pipe was channeled through the joists to the exterior back yard. The problem was that this vent was power driven and all make up air had to come from the basement. The people living in the home would, due to the odors, shut the door to the basement. This only aggravated the odor problem. The furnace sucking action sucked the basement for air. It also sucked the mold spores that existed behind the knotty pine paneling and produced odor. The basement was de-pressurized. We opened the old chimney clean out that was located in the basement. Remarkably, the odor levels were minimized. The client never did remove this knotty pine paneling.

The client performed a temporary interim control. He connected a furnace make-up air vent to equalize the pressure in the basement. He sealed all the cracks on the knotty pine paneling with an expandable caulk. He then painted this knotty pine paneling with several coats of white paint. Although the odor stopped, mold still may be amplifying behind the paneling. This client will still have to deal with this mold issue in the future.

image 14.94

Mold is on the surface of the plank paneling in the basement room (two photographs on this page). There is little or no air circulation in the basement area. The selected panels had a white mold on them. When the panels were removed, there was a considerable amount of moisture and visible black mold on the drywall backer. Testing indicated that the white mold was *Penicillium* and the black molds were *Cladosporium* and *Stachybotrys*. This particular case went into litigation for nondisclosure of water damage. It is always advisable to check all surfaces with a moisture meter and to raise or lift wallpaper and paneling if there are loose or deteriorated locations that are visible. Do not guess. Good science is always backed up with fact.

Site Observation

A steam pipe failed and caused major damage to one unit in an apartment building. The maintenance crew started to demolish all damaged building components. The photos show the contamination on piled up debris within the unit. The maintenance crew were contaminating the entire building during their demolition phase. When they started to rip out walls and floors, they were causing major airborne contamination. They did not use proper abatement or removal protocol. When demolishing mold, all contaminated construction materials and all other contaminated items should be bagged with six-mil polyethylene bags. The construction debris was left indoors and allowed to amplify and cause major spore contamination.

image 14.95

Conclusion

Air testing resulted in the identification of significant indoor contamination. This entire unit had to be isolated and negative air was applied. Air scrubbers were used to help clean the air in other units. All debris was double bagged with six-mil polyethylene bags. After removal of this debris, the construction project resumed. Contractors that do repairs and mold abatement must be trained and qualified. These individuals must implement worker protection. Respirators and proper clothes must be worn on projects that have a high potential to release air-borne mold spores, especially during demolition.

image 14.96

Event

The microbial investigator samples mold behind lath within a wall cavity.

Site Observation

A multiple building complex had a steam boiler heating system. The tenant that lived in the lowest unit was complaining that her windows were always fogged up and mold was growing on the window trim. The landlord received a significantly higher water bill and gas bills. Management could not identify the problem or the location of this problem. Inspectors were called to investigate these conditions. They pressure tested the boiler and found that a breach was occurring. They used an infrared temperature gauge to determine where the leak existed. They found that the kitchen wall was fifteen degrees warmer than the other unit walls. They removed the kitchen counter and cut the floor open. This unit has a sixteen-inch crawl space that was not accessible without cutting the floor. We found an elbow that was dripping on the soil below. The soil was saturated and high humidity existed. We opened several other walls and found significant mold growth.

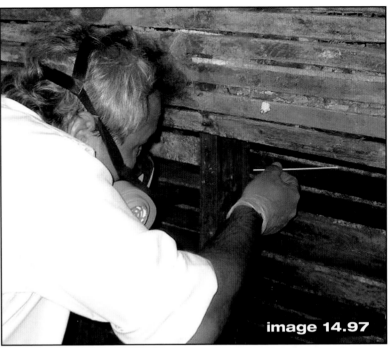

image 14.97

Conclusion

This turned out to be a serious problem. The saturated soil below the unit was causing high humidity in the upper unit. This was the reason why the windows were fogged. It took management three months to figure out what was wrong due to the water billing cycle being only quarterly. The pipes below the floor were rusted due to sweating and poor ventilation. Age, rust, and initial boiler ignition cause the elbow to fail. Three months of leaking was a long time and severe contamination occurred. The crawl moisture caused mold to grow under the entire unit; furthermore, this building was a balloon framed structure and moisture traveled up between stud walls.

image 14.98

This is the hole we made to further identify and expose the damage and microbial contamination below the floor systems.

image 14.99

There is always mold in the soils underneath and surroundings any structure. This was identified to be Stachybotrys by tape lift analysis.

Site Observation

This sump pump failed due to the float getting wedged against the sump pit wall. The basement flooded and allowed the basement wood floor to become saturated. The owners were living in their Florida home at the time of the sump failure. Luckily, the laundry room had a floor drain.

Sump pumps fail frequently for many reasons. You should always see if you have any other floor drains in the basement that are independent of the sump pump. Make sure that these drains have no way of getting plugged up with basement debris. The best safety mechanism is a battery or water-pressure back-up sump pump system.

image 14.100

Conclusion

Every time the sump pump failed, some water would travel under the wood floor. After several months of this condition, we did not test the roots due to the client's budget. The home had a dehumidifier and no other locations had bio-growth. All the floors on the basement level were abated and treated for mold.

image 14.101

Electricity was terminated leaving no power to the sump.

Site Observation

This was a real estate owned property (REO). When we drove up to this property, we could actually "smell the mold" in the front yard. The lower level was contaminated with black slimy mold. Many of these molds were identified as mycotoxic and dangerous. The mold infected the entire home including attic. All REO properties are foreclosures or repossessions. The past owners get evicted and generally trash the home. The utility companies turn off the utilities then the sump pumps cannot work. If it rains, the home can become flooded. The home is vacant and VHS (vacant home syndrome) takes the home over. The result is microbial contamination throughout.

Conclusion

The microbial growth was so significant that the entire interior was removed. All that were left were the studs and joists. After removal of drywall and sheathing, the home was inspected. Remarkably, all of the wood structural components were clean and free of visible mold.

All timbers were sanitized and HEPA vacuumed. The entire structure was encapsulated with paint.

It is prudent to install a battery backup sump pump.

image 14.102

image 14.103

Event

Mold under the front porch is in a hidden room that housed a well casing.

Site Observation

This room was 100% concealed by wall panels. The new owner of this home never knew this room existed. The only symptom was the paneling in the adjacent room had mold and mildew at the base. The entire room in which the access to this room was located smelled moldy. We sounded the wall and found it to be hollow. A digital camera was put into a cut hole for these images. Many homes have old wells in the basements. Porches or stoops that are usually made of concrete generally cover these wells.

Conclusion

The moisture was not coming from the well. The moisture was leaking into the walls from poor exterior drainage. Once in the confined space, the moisture was trapped. City water was installed and the well was plugged. The entrance to the room was covered and forgotten. The moisture from the failed drainage system infiltrated through the cement block walls. This was the beginning of the habitat needed to begin mold amplification. The nutrients were from the soils and cellulose debris in the area. Spores thrived and amplified.

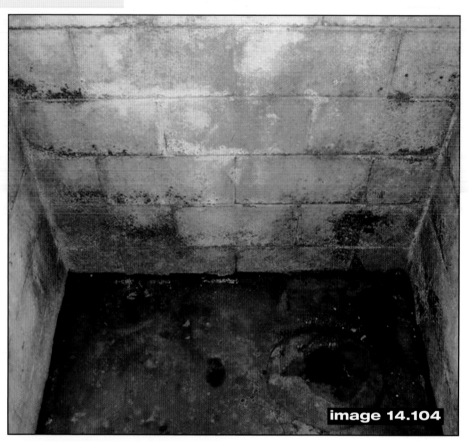

image 14.104

image 14.105

Mold found under front entrance porch.

Site Observations

This was a small cellar room below the front entrance. Water leaked from the concrete ceiling and from the walls. The walls were painted and black mold was growing on them. This room was located on east side of the home. This room, along with the entire home, had severe odors.

The mold condition at this location was caused by front entrance slab leaks. The ceiling was a concrete suspended slab that had shrinkage cracks. Water leaked through these ceiling cracks an into the basement. The foundation was also leaking due to the failed water proofing system.

Conclusion

The homeowner had to waterproof the entire front step area. The three front steps had to be removed, and replaced for this repair. The exterior walls were patched, sealed and parged. The drain-tile system was replaced. The entire suspended slab was sealed with an epoxy coating so it would no longer leach and absorb moisture. The interior mold was removed and all wood shelving was discarded. It was discarded due to significant mold reservoirs that were amplifying on these cellulose products. A dehumidifier was placed in this room and set to 50 % relative humidity. When humidity levels are lower than 50%, mold reservoirs have a difficult time amplifying.

image 14.106

image 14.107

Event

A second floor bathroom leak.

Site Observation

This home had a bathroom plumbing leak. The moisture was trapped in the walls, floors and ceilings. This home was never de-watered. The home was closed up and the electricity was terminated. The home was vacant and no longer maintained. The gutters were dirty and started to spill at the foundation. Some moisture leaked into the basement. This water and residual trapped moisture caused high indoor humidity. The power was off and there was no dehumidification. Vacant Home Syndrome occurred.

Conclusion

The result of VHS is fungal growth and amplification. Thousands of homes throughout the country look like this. The banks sell these homes cheap to investors. Investors clean and paint them. The investors then put these improperly abated homes back on the open market for some innocent first time homebuyer. They buy this mold spore infected home and possibly become sick or sensitized. The walls and the ceilings must be removed and replaced.

image 14.108

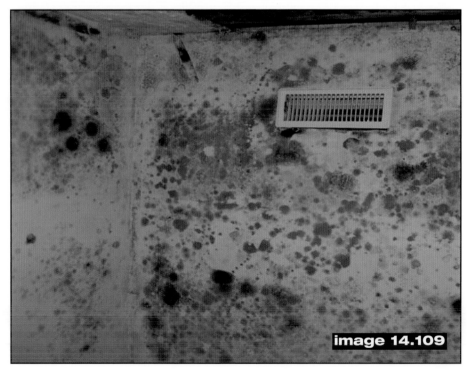

image 14.109

Event

Site Observation

When we entered this home, we smelled a musty odor. No visual mold was seen until you entered into the basement. The basement was 100% mold-covered. At this point we looked around and realized that we were not wearing any PPE (personal protection equipment) This home was full of *Penicillium,* *Aspergillus,* and *Stachybotrys.* A perfectly healthy individual can become sensitized for life from exposures like this.

Conclusion

Anyone that enters and previews vacant contaminated homes is exposed to potential mycotoxins or allergenic molds. It is imperative that all personnel that enter potentially contaminated homes wear personal protection equipment PPE's. At minimum, a respirator should be worn. Dust masks are not adequate and should not be used for mold protection.

For your own protection it is advisable to carry and wear a respirator that is rated PL 100 or equivalent. A magenta colored cartridge should be effective when entering such conditions. However, there are those that only use carbon cassettes on their respirators. Respirable particles can cause lung disorders. Parents should be cautioned about bringing children into these homes.

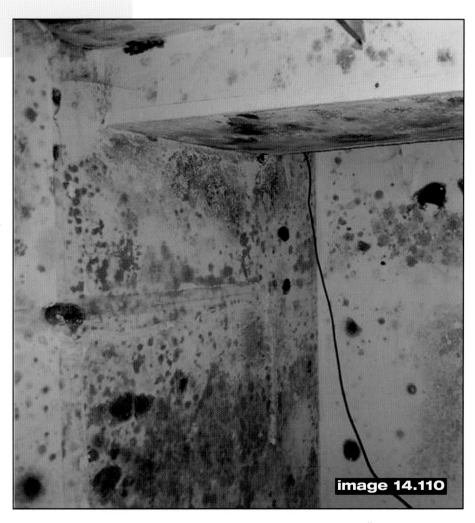

image 14.110

image 14.111

Event

More contaminated bathroom walls.

SITE OBSERVATION

This gives a dirty bathroom a new definition. Believe it or not, this bathroom was actively used, as shown by college students. No fan, no window, no air exchanges, and a bunch of showers. An obvious severe mold problem.

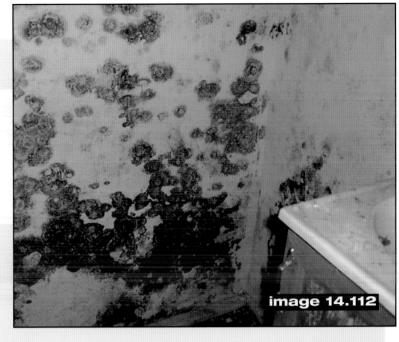

image 14.112

Ten Commandments of the bathroom!

I. Thou shall keep the shower curtain inside of tub.
II. Thou shall keep the shower door closed.
III. Thou shall dry up the floor when done.
IV. Thou shall use waterproof curtains.
V. Thou shall pick up wet towels.
VI. Thou shall keep the bathroom rug clean.
VII. Thou shall not use cornstarch bath powder because it is a nutrient for microorganisms.
VIII. Thou shall replace toilet wax seal when needed.
IX. Thou shall fix all plumbing leaks and not use panty hose for leak repairs or use buckets under the sinks.
X. Thou shall call an electrician and tell him to install an operable exhaust fan to help in the control of bathroom moisture.

image 14.113

Event

Tornados set stage for mold contamination, News at eleven.

Site Condition

These photos were taken roughly eighteen days after a tornado struck this quiet neighborhood.

Conclusion

These homes are not protected from the weather. During the eighteen days prior to taking these digital images, it rained three times and snowed once. Mold will start forming colonies after twenty-four hours. These homes will now need more than just new roofs and new windows. You can download meteorological reports for any part of the country during any time period. The meteorological reports have vital information that can help solve investigations. By knowing humidity and temperatures, you can do psychrometric projections. You can determine if dew points or condensation may have occurred on certain dates. This type of information can sometimes help date microbial contaminations.

image 14.114

image 14.115

image 14.116

Mold suspected behind the drywall.

Site Observation

This home was professionally de-watered and the mold mitigated. We were performing a post abatement visual and air tests. The air tests had high amounts of mold spores that were in greater amounts in the interior than that of the exterior. The home was visually clean and no mold was observed. The homeowners did state that they had a musty odor only at twelve to three p.m. in the afternoon on certain days. This was very odd and strange.

Conclusion

After some time, we were able to figure out what happened. When the attic temperature reached 105° F., the attic exhaust fan would turn on, due to it being on a thermostat. This condition would depressurize the home and suck interstitial air. The odor was coming from the basement walls while the attic fan was on. The home only had an attic fan with no other attic ventilation. It was sucking air from the finished rooms. We cut the wall and found severe contamination. Image 14.118 is a picture of the wall cavity itself after the finished sheetrock was cut. The abatement company failed to identify that there was mold in the wall cavity.

image 14.117

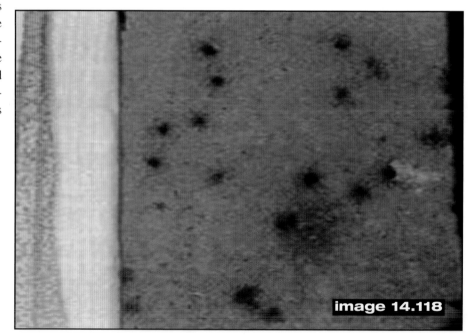

image 14.118

Event

Site Observation

The gutters were not maintained. The roof had poor ventilation. The insulation was not evenly distributed in the attic. The home had all the traits needed to form ice dams. The mold on the ceilings was caused by water from the melting ice dams. This is a serious problem. Moisture and mold within the wall is highly probable when these conditions occur. Image 14.119 shows a chimney-flashing leak.

Conclusion

Moisture meters or infrared imaging equipment is needed to determine the extent of moisture. All drywall that is, or was wet, must be removed. The fungal growth was made available to the interior of the house from the exterior of the dwelling, and amplified by the water activity caused by the water infiltration through capillary action. This activity is due to the ability of water to wick into locations of lesser moisture.

image 14.119

image 14.120

SECTION FIFTEEN
Field Tips and Helpful Hints

PRACTICAL FIELD HINTS TO IMPROVE PROFICIENCY AND SAVE TIME

Event

Signs that keep people out and mold in.

Conclusion

A mold remediation sign should be placed on the exterior side of the door. If signs are not posted, then the general public can enter and become exposed.

The lower sign was used on one of our microbial abatement sites. The term used was BIO-HAZARD CLEANING. The adjacent property owners were not comfortable and made many phone calls to all types of people. The other sign MOLD REMEDIATION IN PROGRESS is less alarming to the general public and should be used. Proper containment is very important and should be at the remediation sites to limit microbial contamination.

image 15.2

image 15.1

BIO-HAZARD CLEANING

DO NOT ENTER

CAUTION

MOLD REMEDIATION IN PROGRESS

DO NOT ENTER

Event

Young parents have a concern that the baby is breathing moldy air.

Site Observations

There was mold found in the basement of a home that had an open cold air return (Cleveland Drop); i.e., no cold air returns attached the air handler.

On site we developed a strategy for testing. This is all done when you sit with the clients and interview them. After the interview, we establish an investigative scope and protocols. These are then written into the report so there is no misunderstanding of exactly what is to be done.

The photos to the right and below are of the investigators reviewing the drawings for a gaming casino that was having air quality problems. Again, we interviewed the clients and developed a scope. This was then followed throughout the thousands of feet of casino and the catwalks above the gaming floor.

Conclusion

Moving equipment, placement of the test devices, batteries, checklists, everything has to be detailed and tailored to the investigation site.

image 15.3

image 15.4

image 15.5

image 15.6

Event

Lower level underground mechanical chase in a high rise building contaminated with unknown slime.

Site Condition

Full body protection was needed to do the investigation. The microbial inspector had to climb fifteen feet down into this location to get laboratory samples. Full body Tyvek, gloves, boots, hat, and a HEPA half-face respirator is the protective gear needed to accomplish this task (Image 15.9). This mechanical chase was three stories below grade. No one has entered this location, since the construction of the building twenty-five years ago. The foundation was leaking, the room was totally dark, and construction debris was scattered on the ground. There was minimal air movement. The lab results identified fifteen different genera of mold.

image 15.7

Conclusion

The contaminates in Image 15.7 were a witch's brew of bio-growth, bacterial growth, slime, and efflorescence salts. They were all growing or attached to construction debris that served as amplifiers on the wet slimy floor, probably from initial construction twenty years ago. Carry protective gear at all times because you never know what you will find. Most buildings will have underground chases, runways, utility halls, and etc. You should always check with building management and view the building prints prior to starting a microbial investigation in large facilities.

image 15.8

Properly dispose of all your contaminated protective clothing.

image 15.9

Site Condition

Viable air testing is recommended when performing legal investigations. Viable air results will tell you how many live mold spores exist in the air at the time of testing. A pump will suck a given amount of volume of air, at an impaction flow rate, and impact the mold spores into a Petri dish. The dish is cultured at 20° to 30° C. A Microscopist will prepare slides and identify and count the colonies. The results will be in a number amount per volume. Typically these results are in how many spores per cubic meter of air. (EX: 1200 Spores of *Mucor*/m3) This means that you breathe 1200 spores of Mucor per cubic meter of air in this dwelling. A second viable air test needs to be done on the exterior of the test site. You need to know what the conditions are on the exterior. (EX 20 Spores or *Mucor*/m3) You need to subtract the exterior sources and amounts from the interior amounts. The final amount or corrected amount would be 1180 counts of *Mucor*/M3 of air indoors. These tests are taken at a rate of 28.3 liters per minute at a time of three to four minutes.

Conclusion

Viable air testing is generally necessary when you are performing legal work due to opposing experts; generally being industrial hygienists, engineers, microscopists, micro-biologists and other educated professionals.

These professionals will challenge your mold report if some viable testing has not been done. It is our experience that you need to implement several methodologies.

Tape lifts, swab testing, Air-O-Cell cassettes and Anderson viable tests are a good mixture.

In legal work you will need to be able to define how much contamination exists and determine if there is more contamination inside, than that of the exterior clean environment. A mold found in a settlement plate will tell the courts nothing other than that mold is on the dish. You may as well set out a cup of coffee and look at it after three days. To practice good science and do good legal work, you need to perform several different tests and use several different laboratories. Finally, once you obtain all the results you will need to form a conclusion. Quantification and qualification are necessary when providing a standard of care and due diligence. You must practice good science.

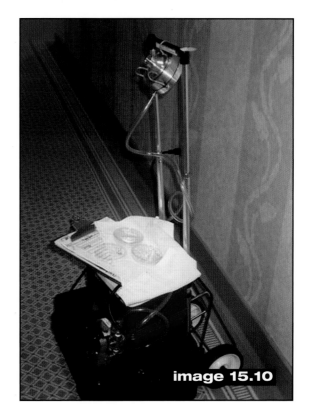

image 15.10

Your Daughter or Grand-daughter

One Spore

39.37"

1 Cubic meter 39.37 inches per side

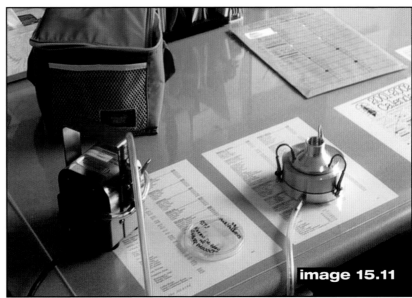

image 15.11

Site Observation

This was a single unit that existed in a ten-unit building.

Conclusion

Using a sling psychrometer seems a bit prehistoric when you have electronic gauges that tell you everything you need to know with a push of the button. Many times, the electronic gauges are slightly off or inaccurate. You should always take at least two additional tests using a sling to establish a base line or a calibration of your electronic gauge. You always want to take a reading in both the clean control area and the exterior environment.

The sling will give you a wet bulb[1] temperature and a dry bulb[2] temperature. With these two values you can determine the humidity. These gauges can be purchased for less than one hundred dollars.[3]

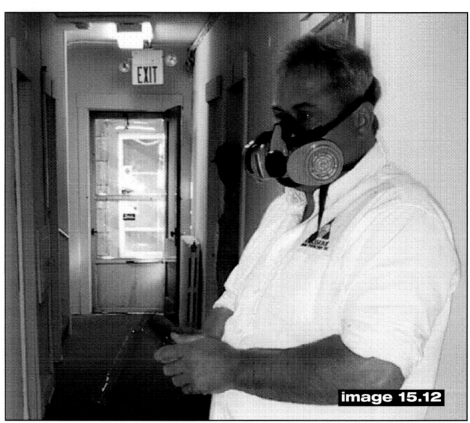

image 15.12

---

[1] *Wet Bulb Temperature*

The temperature reading that results when a thermometer's sensing bulb is fitted with sock saturated with water and placed in an air stream. As the water evaporates heat is removed from the bulb thereby reducing the temperature reading. When a condition of dynamic equilibrium is reach the rate of heat transferred from the passing air stream to the water equals the heat transferred from the water to the air stream via the evaporated water.

[2] *Dry Bulb Temperature*

Simply the temperature of the air stream or sample as measured by any standard temperature measurement device.

[3] Call Professional Equipment Co-see acknowledgements

Event

Investigator is testing the air for humidity conditions using a portable sling psychrometer and electronic gauge.

Site Observation

Always check the humidity of a home. The oldest and easiest gauge to use is a sling psychrometer. All you need to do is follow the simple directions. This gauge tells you what the humidity is in the home that is in question.

This gauge is easy to use and costs less than one hundred dollars. You should have one of these units if you will be calculating humidity indoors. After you use this unit for fifteen minutes, your hand will become sore. It is very physical to use. Having a second electronic gauge is advised. Many companies make these units.

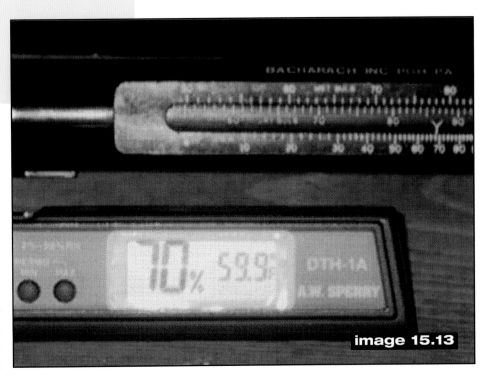

image 15.13

Conclusion

You need to have both gauges. The sling is never wrong but will tire your hand. The electronic unit is usually accurate, but can be biased if bumped or damaged. Use the sling for your first and last readings to keep your electronic unit calibrated. This is a good quality control measure.
(SEE PSYCHROMETRIC CHART SECTION)

image 15.14

Event

Peeling paint and efflorescence in the basement.

Site Observation

One of the indicators of possible moisture intrusion is a white, powdery or crystalline substance sometimes found on the surface of concrete, plaster, or masonry.

Conclusion

Known as efflorescence, it occurs as water containing soluble salts evaporate from the surface of an object. On exterior surfaces it is usually only an aesthetic concern. When found indoors, however, it indicates a water or moisture intrusion which could lead to mold amplification and possibly structural damage. The soluble salts originate from the building materials themselves or from the ground. As water travels through the soil, wall, or building foundation, it dissolves the salts, transporting them to the surface. Then, as the water evaporates, it leaves the salts behind. These deposits are usually white, but can also be green, brown or gray depending on mineral composition. Efflorescence will continue as long as there is a source of salts and water. Often, salt sources are eventually exhausted, and exterior efflorescence disappears by itself over time with normal weathering. A speedier cleanup can be accomplished by washing the surface with water or diluted muriatic acid and a stiff brush (non-white stains should not be washed with acid as staining could occur). Note that water can re-dissolve salts and transport them back into the building material, allowing further efflorescence. Applications of acid should be preceded by a wetting of the surface and followed with a water or alkaline-and-water rinse. Be sure to consult professional guidelines before handling any acid, and follow proper safety precautions.

image 15.15

Moisture moves from here at the wall floor intersection...

Unlike exterior efflorescence, interior salt deposits should be addressed immediately; they are signs of ground water intrusion, leaky pipes, and defective drains, etc. Careful analysis of the situation is important not only to determine the cause of water intrusion, but also to determine if mold amplification has occurred. If, upon analysis, no mold is found, removal of the water source should still occur immediately to prevent potential future fungal growth.

It is an interesting journey, from efflorescence and moisture infiltration to mold contamination on a dwelling's building components.

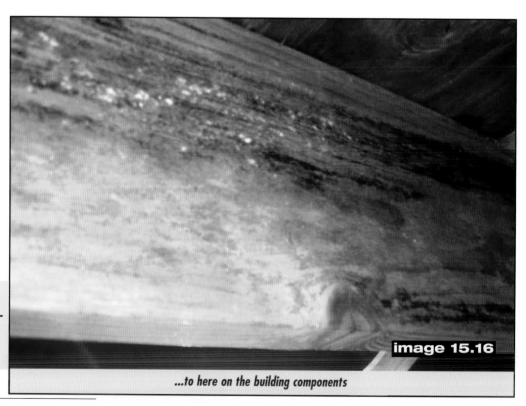

image 15.16

...to here on the building components

[1] *IAQ and Efflorescence ever wonder what that white stuff is? by Paul Cochrane*

Event

Mold in an un-heated garage with no insulation.

Site Observations

Ventilation systems are designed and installed in buildings to replace stale, contaminated air with fresh air from the outside. Air enters and leaves a house in several other ways, too. It can enter by infiltration, through construction joints and cracks around windows and doors, through the foundation, and crawl spaces. Air also enters through natural ventilation openings; such as, open doors and windows. The rate at which outdoor air replaces indoor air is the "exchange rate." It measures how many times the complete volume of air inside the house is replaced with fresh outside air. In typical U.S. homes, the average exchange rate is 0.7 to 1.0 complete air exchanges per hour. In tight homes, the exchange rate can be as low as 0.02 complete air exchanges per hour. In leaky homes it may be as high as two complete air changes per hour.

Mold problems are more common in summer and gradually decline from September through November.

Conclusion

Without air exchanges in the dwelling, and this includes the crawl spaces, mold spores can develop due to the unconditioned air and the presence of moisture on the substrate material.

image 15.17

image 15.18

image 15.19

Conclusion

Did you know if you find a new mold you could give it a name? If you study a mold and conclude with significant findings, you can put your name after the genus name. If you find a new species, you can add your name as a suffix.

Example *Stachybotrys* is a genus name. Atra is a specie name. Research on *Stachybotrys* further identified that it was paper-loving. For many years, *Stachybotrys* was called *Stachybotrys* atra. Chartarum was added after further research on *Stachybotrys* and now the famous black mold is called *Stachybotrys* chartarum. This is why you have hundreds of different species of Aspergilli. Many scientists study this genus and find new species in homes. We generally find approximately 40 different species. Generally only four to twelve genera are identified on test results. Although thousands of mold types exist, we usually find common indoor mold that is associated with indoor moisture problems. The red outline of the mold contamination resembles a famous singer. Myron, the Microscopist, gave this mold a new name. Amerimold elvislookalykus.

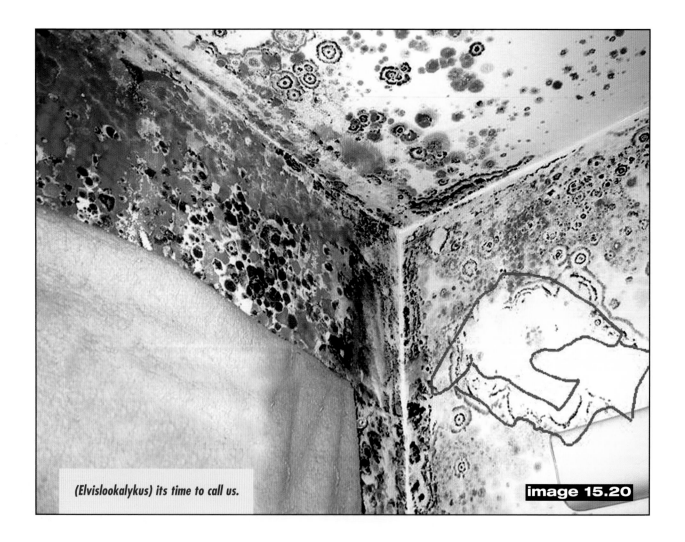

(Elvislookalykus) its time to call us.

image 15.20

Site Condition

In the upper digital image (15.21), a microbial investigator is sampling the wall with a swab. When you sample using this method, you will disturb the mold on the wall and release spores. This is why tape lifts are the way to fly. With both the swabs and the tape lifts, you must be careful not to press very hard. Pressing hard can damage the sample or make it difficult for the microscopist to evaluate. You should also take the sample from the outer edges where the mold spores are vegetative and blooming. The center, darker areas may no longer be viable or living. In the lower digital image (15.22), the investigator is using a tape-lift kit. This method does not release or disturb the spores as much as the swab testing does. Here, the investigator gently presses the tape-lift system on the sample. You should be wearing PPE, personal protection equipment.

image 15.21

Conclusion

Always fill out the chain of custody paperwork properly. Document and label everything. Always include a copy for your records. Record keeping is a critical part of "good science."

image 15.22

SECTION SIXTEEN

Health Effects

POSSIBLE HEALTH EFFECTS

Q: Are some molds more hazardous than others are?

A: Allergic persons vary in their sensitivities to mold, both as to the amount and type needed to cause reactions. In addition, certain types of molds can produce toxins, called mycotoxins, that the mold uses to inhibit or prevent the growth of other organisms. Mycotoxins are found in both living and dead mold spores. Materials permeated with mold need to be removed, even after they are disinfected with cleaning solutions. Allergic and toxic effects can remain in dead spores. Exposure to mycotoxins may present a greater hazard than that of allergenic or irritative molds. Mycotoxins have been found in homes, agricultural settings, food, and office buildings.[1]

Q: What are some of the health effects?

A: Allergic reactions are the most common health problems associated with biological pollutants. Symptoms often include watery eyes, runny nose and sneezing, nasal congestion, itching, coughing and wheezing, along with difficulty breathing, headache, dizziness and fatigue. Dust mites have been identified as the single most important trigger for asthma attacks.[2]

Q: What are the health effects from biological pollutants?

A: Allergic reactions are the most common health problem associated with biological pollutants. People differ in their sensitivity to biological allergens -- some may have no symptoms, while sensitive persons may have severe health problems. Common symptoms include watery eyes, runny nose and sneezing, nasal congestion, itching, coughing, and wheezing along with difficulty breathing, headache, dizziness and fatigue.

The most severe reaction to allergens is an asthma attack, which can be life-threatening. The American Lung Association reports there are nearly 10 million people in the U.S. with asthma. Of these, over 2.5 million are children. There are over 4,000 deaths each year from asthma. The number of persons with asthma has been consistently increasing over the last 15 years. Airborne biological pollutants present a special risk to people with allergies and asthma.

Note: these pollutants do not cause asthma. Rather, certain pollutants can trigger an attack in people who have asthma.

Infectious diseases caused by bacteria and viruses are generally passed from person to person through physical contact. Some bacteria and viruses circulate through indoor ventilation systems.[3]

The following page contains a listing of health conditions relative to indoor air quality.[4]

---

[1] California Department of Health Services
[2] Minnesota Department of Health Indoor Air Program
[3] Kansas State University Extension Service
[4] Enviro Team, Inc. Fort Lauderdale FL. Much of the information taken for this section came from the IAQA and CIE Course handbook from modules 3, 4, and 5 that was offered in Ft. Lauderdale, Florida, November 11-15, 2002. This course was taught by professionals of the Enviro Team.

Allergic Asthma

This disease is characterized by airway obstruction, airway (air tubes) inflammation and airway responsiveness to a variety of stimuli. The three basic factors that can occur to block the airways are: muscles around the air tubes constrict, an inflammation and swelling of the lining occurs, and an increase in mucus flow clogs the air tubes. At this time roughly 10% of the population in the USA has this disease. Asthma can be triggered from allergens, irritants, cold air, weather changes, infection, exercise, aspirin, foods, emotional upset, and dust mites.

Allergic Bronchopulmonary Aspergillosis

This is an allergic disease that is caused by a specific immune response to *Aspergillus* species of fungi. It is also related to the disease *Aspergillus* sinusitis.

Allergic Contact Dermatitis

This is a common skin condition related to an allergy that is associated with the cellular immune response. Contact dermatitis accounts for about 30% of all patients seeking treatment in dermatology clinics. Most cases are a result of direct contact with the offending agent, however there have been reports of cases in which Bioaerosols were involved[5].

Allergic Rhinitis

Rhinitis is inflammation of the mucosa lining of the nose. Allergic rhinitis (hay fever) is caused by the IgE[6] mediated inflammation. Some symptoms include nasal congestion, post nasal drip, runny nose and sneezing. At this time, this disease affects over 12% of the USA population.

Allergy

An allergy is a state or immune hypersensitivity that presents itself to the susceptible individual who upon exposure to an "antigen" responds with an overproduction of certain immune system components, such as, immunoglobin E (IgE) antibodies. An antigen is a substance that stimulates the production of an antibody.

Atopy

Atopy is generally defined as the state of having one or more of a defined group of diseases that are caused by the genetic predisposition to produce IgE antibodies when exposed to environmental allergens. Exposure may occur through the lungs, GI tract, and skin contact.

Chronic Bronchitis

This is a chronic cough that is present more that 50% of the time for a period of two years.

Humidifier Fever

This is a disease that presents flu like symptoms after exposure to microbial agents living in humidifiers. Affected individuals may experience headache, rhinitis, asthma and lethargy.

Hypersensitivity Pneumonitis (HP)

This is a lung disease that is very complex. It causes an inflammatory response which may result from inhaling organic materials; such as, common fungi or bacteria that are present in the environment. Some symptoms of HP are shortness of breath and non-productive cough. In acute episodes fever and chills along with respiratory symptoms may be present.

Hypersensitivity

Type 1 Reactions are generally rapid, seconds to minutes and may result in allergic rhinitis or and asthma response.

Type 2 Reactions are a little slower, minutes to hours and may result in an immunologic pulmonary hemorrhagic syndrome.

Type 3 Reactions are in approximately 30 minutes to two hours and may induce hypersensitivity pneumonitis.

Type 4 Reactions are delayed. The time is estimated at 18 to maybe 24 hours or so. The response may be hypersensitivity pneumonitis asthma.

Immunocompromised Individual

This is an individual that has a lowered resistance to fight off the infection. An example of an immunocompromised individual is someone that is on chemotherapy, a diabetic on antibiotics, an asthmatic, an HIV positive, an Aids patient, or one with normal immune function.

Sinusitis

This is an inflammation of the sinuses, which are "channels," that surround the nasal cavity. Symptoms include rhinitis, facial pressure, sore throat, bad breath, cough and nasal secretions. The Department of Health and Human Services data (1981) shows that 31 million individuals suffer from chronic sinusitis.

The above sickness can be linked to airborne and fungal contamination.[7]

---

[5] Indoor Allergens, Institute of Medicine National Academy Press

[6] Immunoglobin E

[7] Enviro Team, Inc. Fort Lauderdale FL. Much of the information taken for this section came from the IAQA and CIE Course handbook from modules 3, 4, and 5 that was offered in Ft. Lauderdale, Florida, November 11-15, 2002. This course was taught by professionals of the Enviro Team.

SECTION SEVENTEEN
Select molds and information

MORE THAN MOST PEOPLE NEED TO KNOW ABOUT MOLDS

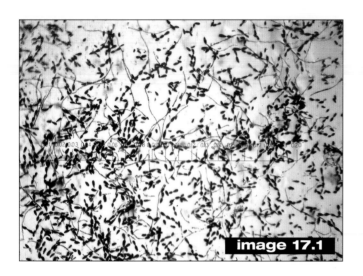

image 17.1

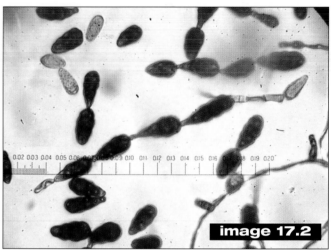

image 17.2

Alternaria sp. - Extremely widespread and ubiquitous. Outdoors it may be isolated from samples of soil, seeds, and plants. It is commonly found in outdoor samples. It is often found in carpets, textiles, and on horizontal surfaces in building interiors. Often found on window frames. The species *Alternaria* alternata is capable of producing tenuazonic acid and other toxic metabolites which may be associated with disease in humans or animals. *Alternaria* produces large spores having sizes between 20 - 200 microns in length and 7 - 18 microns in width, suggesting that the spores from this fungi are deposited in the nose, mouth, and upper respiratory tract. It may be related to bakers' asthma. It has been associated with hypersensitivity pneumonitis, sinusitis, deratomycosis, onychomycosis, subcutaneous phaeohyphomycosis, and invasive infection. Common cause of extrinsic asthma (immediate-type hypersensitivity: type I). Acute symptoms include edema and bronchiospasms, chronic cases may develop pulmonary emphysema.

Arthrinium sp. - Widespread saprophyte on dead plant material, particularly swampy grasses. Should be considered an allergen. This fungus has also been documented in various subcutaneous infections. No toxic related diseases are on record to date.

Ascomycete sp. - One of the major classes of fungal organisms. This class contains the "sac fungi" and yeasts. Some *Ascomycete* spores can be identified by spore morphology, however; some care should be exercised with regard to specific identification. Many *Ascomycete* spores are reported to be allergenic.

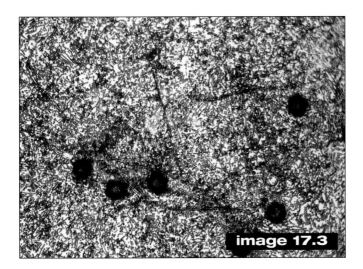

image 17.3

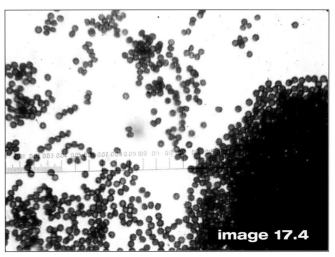

image 17.4

Aspergillus sp. - A genus of fungi containing approximately 150 recognized species. Members of this genus have been recovered from a variety of habitats, but are especially common as saprophytes on decaying vegetation, soils, stored food, and feed products in tropical and subtropical regions. Some species are parasitic on insects, plants and animals, including man. Species within this genus have reported Aw's (water activities) between 0.75 - 0.82. All of the species contained in this genus should be considered allergenic. Various *Aspergillus* species are a common cause of extrinsic asthma (immediate-type hypersensitivity: type I). Acute symptoms include edema and bronchiospasms. Chronic cases may develop pulmonary emphysema. Members of this genus are reported to cause a variety of opportunistic infections of the ears and eyes. Sever pulmonary infections may also occur. Many species produce mycotoxins which may be associated with disease in humans and other animals. Toxin production is dependent on the species or a strain within a species and on the food source for the fungus. Some of these toxins have been found to be carcinogenic in animal species. Several toxins are considered potential human carcinogens.

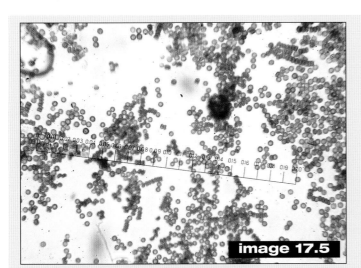

image 17.5

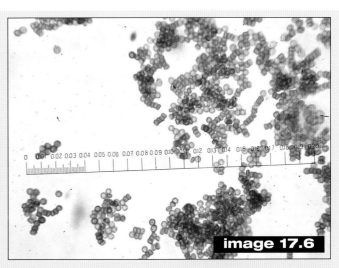

image 17.6

Aureobasidium sp. - A cosmopolitan fungus with the main habitat apparently on the aerial parts of plants. Frequently found in moist environments. This fungus should be considered allergenic. This species has been associated with deratitis, peritonitis, pulmonary infection, and invasive disease in AIDS patients. Probably acquired by traumatic implantation. May be recovered as a contaminant from human cutaneous sites. No toxic diseases have been documented to date.

Basidiomycete - One of the major classes of fungal organisms. This class contains the mushrooms, shelf fungi, puffballs, and a variety of other macrofungi. It is extremely difficult to identify a specific genera of mushrooms by using standard culture plate techniques. Some *Basidiomycete* spores can be identified by spore morphology, however; some care should be exercised with regard to specific identification. Many *Basidiomycete* spores are reported to be allergenic.

Bipolaris sp. - A widespread fungus that is most frequently associated with grasses, plant material, decaying food, and soil. It is common to both indoor and outdoor environments. Older obsolete names include Drechslera and Helminthosporium. This fungus produces large spores which would be expected to be deposited in the upper respiratory tract. Various species of this fungus can produce the mycotoxin - sterigmatocystin which has been shown to produce liver and kidney damage when ingested by laboratory animals.

Botrytis sp. - It is parasitic on plants, vegetables, and soft fruits but may also be found in soil. Reported to be allergenic. No toxic or invasive diseases have been documented to date.

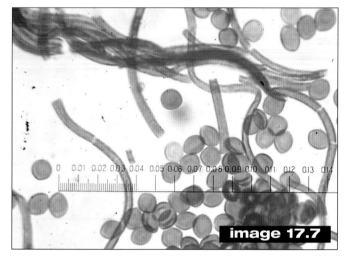

image 17.7

Chaetomium sp. - Large ascomycetous fungus producing perithecia. It is found on a variety of substrates containing cellulose including paper and plant compost. It can be readily found on the damp or water damaged paper in sheetrock.

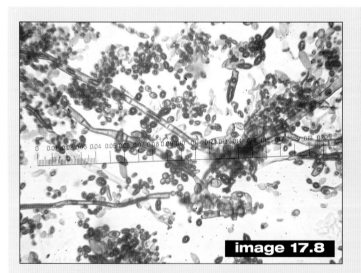

image 17.8

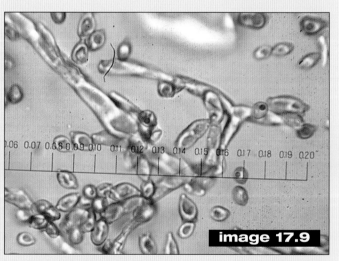

image 17.9

Cladosporium sp. - Aw (water activity) in the range of 0.84 to 0.88. Most commonly identified outdoor fungus. The outdoor numbers are reduced in the winter. The numbers are often high in the summer. Often found indoors in numbers less than outdoor numbers. It is a common allergen. Indoor *Cladosporium* sp. may be different than the species identified outdoors. It is commonly found on the surface of fiberglass duct liner in the interior of supply ducts. A wide variety of plants are food sources for this fungus. It is found on dead plants, woody plants, food, straw, soil, paint and textiles. It can cause mycosis. Produces greater than 10 antigens. Antigens in commercial extracts are of variable quality and may degrade within weeks of preparation. Common cause of extrinsic asthma (immediate-type hypersensitivity: type I). Acute symptoms include edema and bronchiospasms, chronic cases may develop pulmonary emphysema.

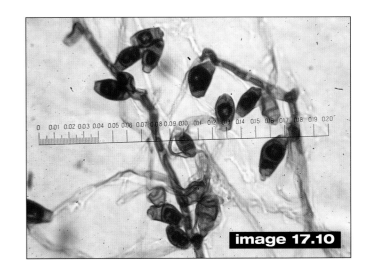
image 17.10

Curvularia sp. - Reported to be allergenic. It may cause corneal infections, mycetoma and infections in immune compromised hosts.

Drechslera sp. - Conidia (spores) dimensions 40-120 x 17-28 microns. Found on grasses, grains and decaying food. It can occasionally cause a corneal infection of the eye.

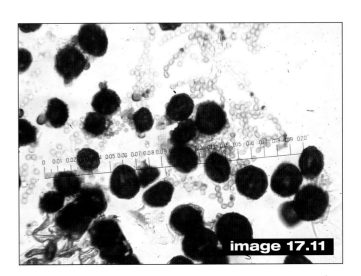
image 17.11

Epicoccum sp. - Conidia (spores) dimensions 15-25 microns. A common allergen. It is found in plants, soil, grains, textiles, and paper products.

Fusarium sp. - Aw (water activity) 0.90. A common soil fungus. It is found on a wide range of plants. It is often found in humidifiers. Several species in this genus can produce potent trichothecene toxins (5, 27). The trichothecene (scirpene) toxin targets the following systems: circulatory, alimentary, skin, and nervous. Produces vomitoxin on grains during unusually damp growing conditions. Symptoms may occur either through ingestion of contaminated grains or possibly inhalation of spores. The genera can produce hemorrhagic syndrome in humans (alimentary toxic aleukia). This is characterized by nausea, vomiting, diarrhea, dermatitis, and extensive internal bleeding. Reported to be allergenic. Frequently involved in eye, skin and nail infections.

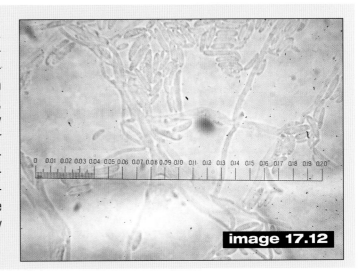
image 17.12

Geotrichum sp. - Aw (water activity) 0.90. Conidia (spores) dimensions 6-12 x 3-6 microns. A common contaminant of grains, fruits, dairy products, paper, textiles, soil and water, and often present as part of the normal human flora. The species *Geotrichum condidum* can cause a secondary infection (geotrichosis) in association with tuberculosis. This rare disease can cause lesions of the skin, bronchi, mouth, lung, and intestine.

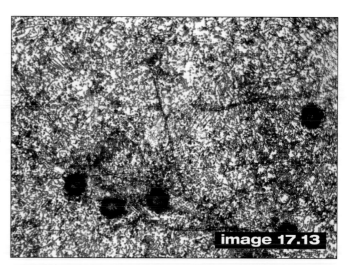

Mucor sp. - Often found in soil, dead plant material, horse dung, fruits, and fruit juice. It is also found in leather, meat, dairy products, animal hair, and jute. A Zygomycetes fungus which may be allergenic (skin and bronchial tests) (7, 17). This organism and other Zygomycetes will grow rapidly on most fungal media. May cause mucorosis in immune compromised individuals. The sites of infection are the lung, nasal sinus, brain, eye, and skin. Infection may have multiple sites.

Penicillium sp. - Aw (water activity) 0.78 - 0.88. A wide number of organisms have placed in this genus. Identification to species is difficult. Often found in aerosol samples. Commonly found in soil, food, cellulose, and grains (17, 5). It is also found in paint and compost piles. It may cause hypersensitivity pneumonitis and allergic alveolitis in susceptible individuals. It is reported to be allergenic (skin) (7, 17). It is commonly found in carpet, wallpaper, and in interior fiberglass duct insulation (NC). Some species can produce mycotoxins. Common cause of extrinsic asthma (immediate-type hypersensitivity: type I). Acute symptoms include edema and bronchiospasms, chronic cases may develop pulmonary emphysema.

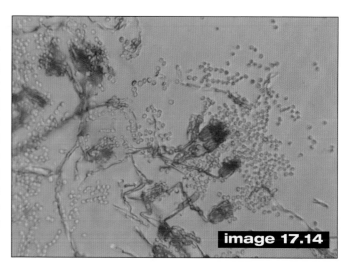

Periconia sp. - No information available.

Phoma sp. - A common indoor air allergen. It is similar to the early stages of growth of *Chaetomium sp*. The species are isolated from soil and associated plants (particularly potatoes). Produces pink and purple spots on painted walls (3, 17). It may have antigens which cross-react with those of *Alternaria sp*. It will grow on butter, paint, cement, and rubber. It may cause phaeohyphomycosis, a systematic or subcutaneous disease.

Pithomyces sp. - Grows on dead grass in pastures. Causes facial eczema in ruminants.

Rhizopus sp. - The Zygomycetes fungus is reported to be allergenic. It may cause mucorosis in immune compromised individuals. It occupies a biological niche similar to Mucor sp. It is often linked to occupational allergy. The sites of infection are the lung, nasal sinus, brain, eye, and skin. Infection may have multiple sites.

Rhodotorula sp. - A reddish yeast typically found in moist environments such as carpeting, cooling coils, and drain pans. In some countries it is the most common yeast genus identified in indoor air. This yeast has been reported to be allergenic. Positive skin tests have been reported. It has colonized in terminally ill patients.

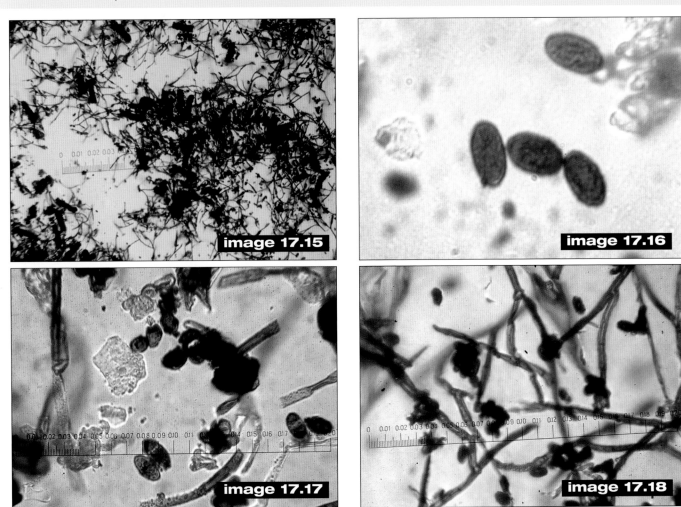

image 17.15

image 17.16

image 17.17

image 17.18

Stachybotrys sp. - Aw (water activity) - 0.94, optimum Aw (water activity) - >0.98. Several strains of this fungus (S. atra, S. chartarum and S. alternans are synonymous) may produce a trichothecene mycotoxin- Satratoxin H - which is poisonous by inhalation. The toxins are present on the fungal spores. This is a slow growing fungus on media. It does not compete well with other rapidly growing fungi. The dark colored fungi grows on building material with a high cellulose content and a low nitrogen content. Areas with relative humidity above 55% and are subject to temperature fluctuations are ideal for toxin production. Individuals with chronic exposure to the toxin produced by this fungus reported cold and flu symptoms, sore throats, diarrhea, headaches, fatigue, dermatitis, intermittent local hair loss, and generalized malaise. The toxins produced by this fungus will suppress the immune system affecting the lymphoid tissue and the bone marrow. Animals injected with the toxin from this fungus exhibited the following symptoms: necrosis and hemorrhage within the brain, thymus, spleen, intestine, lung, heart, lymph node, liver, and kidney. The mycotoxin is also reported to be a liver and kidney carcinogen. Affects by absorption of the toxin in the human lung are known as pneumomycosis. This organism is rarely found in outdoor samples. It is usually difficult to find in indoor air samples unless it is physically disturbed. The spores are in a gelatinous mass. Appropriate media for the growth of this organism will have a high cellulose content and a low nitrogen content. The spores will die readily after release. The dead spores are still allergenic and toxigenic. Percutaneous absorption has caused mild symptoms.

Stemphyllium sp. - Reported to be allergenic. Isolated from dead plants and cellulose materials.

Teliomycetes – Commonly known as true slime molds. They exhibit characteristics of microorganism and fungi. Distributed world wide, they usually occur in decaying plant material. Symptoms occur, either through ingestion of contaminated food, or inhalation of spores. In severe cases, the fungus can produce hemorrhagic syndrome in humans. This is characterized by nausea, vomiting, diarrhea, dermatitis, and extensive internal bleeding.

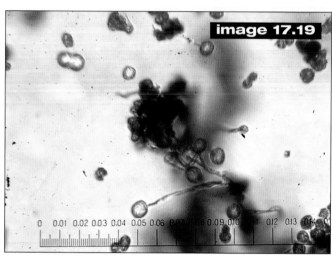

Trichoderma sp. - It is commonly found in soil, dead trees, pine needles, paper, and unglazed ceramics. It often will grow on other fungi. It produces antibiotics which are toxic to humans. It has been reported to be allergenic (7, 17). It readily degrades cellulose.

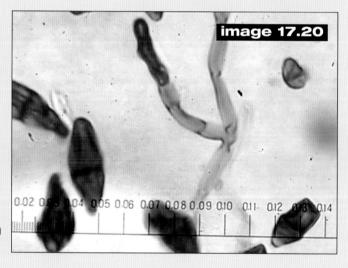

Ulocladium sp. - Has an Aw (water activity) of 0.89. Isolated from dead plants and cellulose materials. Found on textiles.

Yeast - Various yeasts are commonly identified on air samples. Some yeasts are reported to be allergenic. They may cause problems if a person has had previous exposure and developed hypersensitivity. Yeasts may be allergenic to susceptible individuals when present in sufficient concentrations.

KNOW YOUR MOLD...
ASPERGILLIS

Is it just "typical household mold?" Sometimes this statement often follows the finding of mold in the home during a general home inspection. Every one is concerned about the dreaded slimy mold Stachybotrys or its friend Fusarium but more often than not other species can and do carry mycotoxins that can affect us drastically.

Patrick O'Donald, CIE Certified Indoor-air Environmentalist, during a recent class sponsored by the Indoor Air Quality Association[1], made a specific issue both in his presentation and in the course of study learning materials, that *Stachybotrys* is not alone. This constantly ever-present fellow *Aspergillus* is also a mycotoxin[2]. *Aspergillus* is a ubiquitous agent that is found in HVAC systems. *Aspergillus* fumigatus is probably the best known opportunistic pathogen. It can grow in the human respiratory tract and can invade living tissue. There are many species of *Aspergillus* and several of them have been implicated in infectious disease[3]. In humans, "*Aspergillosis*" usually occurs as and infection of the external ear." The top five of the *Aspergillus* molds that are identified in indoor environments are A. versicolor, A. flavus, A. fumigatus, A. auricomus and A. niger[4].

Immune compromised individuals are most susceptible to opportunistic pathogens such as *Aspergillosis*. Examples of an immunocomprised individual is someone who is on chemotherapy, a diabetic on antibiotics, an asthmatic, an HIV positive individual, and also an individual with a physical or mental condition that interferes with normal immune function.

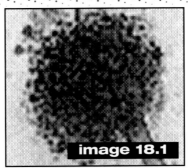

image 18.1

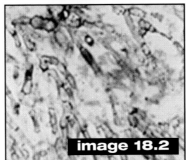

image 18.2

Since this mold has the ability to attach itself to the earwax of unsuspecting creatures, inspectors should consider adequate ear protection before attempting aggressive sampling.

Healthy individuals may be able to resist infection to large doses of these spores. Inhaled spores may be transient colonizers in our bodies causing no harm.

The common name for the disease is *Aspergillosis* and its symptoms are ulceration and perforation of the ear membrane. Make no mistake, you can neither determine a mold species without microscopic review, nor can you quantify it with out a defined quantity of air passing around a slide, tape, or plate.

The interesting phenomenon about *Aspergillus* fumigatus is that it is quite often lumped with *Penicillium* in non-viable Air-O-Cell analysis because they are not distinguishable from each other. Laboratories[5] suggest that viable[6] testing be done to identify Colony Forming Units.

Mr. O'Donald makes a strong point for client and worker protection, i.e. inspector protection, when entering spaces that contain mold or bio-growth activity. He also cautions microbial assessors to be careful about creating an event while using aggressive sampling techniques.

---

[1] The I.A.Q.A. sponsored a class leading to the CIE Certified Indoor-air Environmentalist certification

[2] Aspergillus, a mycotoxin represents several related fungi, which cause Aspergillosis, which represents a group of similar infections.

[3] This disease most often affects the external ear, but also the lungs. Aspergillus species are common in the soil, and spores will be come airborne in dry windy weather. Spores can not only enter and grow in the lungs, eyes, and ears, but also in most areas of buildings and ventilation systems.

[4] By permission of Patrick O'Donald, Enviro Team, Inc.

[5] Miller, Aerotech monitor Volume 4 Issue 3

[5] EMSL laboratories indicates this with all of their reported results

[6] viable is living or growing; vs nonviable

[7] Jeff May is the author of the book *My House Is Killing Me*

Individuals that sample bio-growth need to know more about its characteristics. Inter-disciplinary course work is always recommended. ASHI members like Jeff May[7] are practiced in the bio-growth bio-aerosol field. Inspectors should give mold the same respect they give to electricity. Both, under the right conditions can be helpful or harmful depending on the conditions.

When mold is found, that is the time to ask some appropriate questions and offer direction regarding mold, its health effects, and possible further investigation. Microbial assays and investigations and general home inspections are not in the same category. However the home inspector can provide the necessary client awareness to proceed with a microbial assay.

The Closet Dwellers

One of my favorite radio shows was "Fibber McGee and Molly." This gregarious family inhabited a typical house on Wistful Vista. In the house was a closet named appropriately Fibber McGee's closet! This was a wonderful confined space that contained everything and anything. Usually when Fibber opened this door he was inundated by its contents. Not un-like the closets that we encounter on a daily basis. However, our closets can contain more than household chattel, there could be mold there, microbial VOC's, i.e. that musty smell and mildew.

Mold in the closet? Yes. Closets that are on outside walls that have limited or no circulation are a perfect habitat to cultivate mold spores. The reason why is not complex. It is just something that you should be aware of and why.

We all know that moisture can go anywhere it wants. A classic example of the moisture problem in a heating climate can occur in an enclosed closet on an exterior wall. The closet has a higher ratio of surface area to volume as compared to other condition spaces, resulting in a greater heat loss. It may also be exposed to the wind. If this is an older house, it is most likely poorly insulated and probably colder than the adjacent room because of a high heat loss rate and the fact that it is separated for other conditioned spaces with no apparent independent source of heat.[1]

The vapor pressure[2] of the closet and of the adjacent heated rooms should be the same. However the closet temperature will be lower and the relative humidity will be higher.

Here is an example. If the relative humidity is 35% at a temperature of 70° F at the adjacent conditioned space, there is a low amount of moisture in the conditioned room. If the vapor pressure is the same in both spaces, a closet temperature of 50° results in a relative humidity of 70%. This is now high enough to have mold and mildew growth. If the temperature gets lower in the closet, then it is possible to reach a relative humidity of 100%, or a dew point temperature resulting in condensation and possible component deterioration.

(Closets that are located within the confines of the house and over crawl spaces, can exhibit similar characteristics.) All of these conditions can be plotted on a psychrometric chart[4] on site or at a later date. A psychrometric chart graphically indicates the relationship between dry and wet bulb temperatures, relative humidity, dew point, and on some grains of moisture and enthalpy.

It is also possible to identify the temperature within the wall at a given point by knowing the indoor temperature, the outdoor temperature, the sum of R values[5] prior to the point of concern, and the R values past the point of concern. By using the formula below, the investigator can find the temperature and relate it to the dew point potential at that location.[6]

1. Calculate the total T value of the wall. Call this R1
2. Calculate the R-value of the wall from the inside air to the point P. Call this R2
3. Ti = Indoor temperature
4. To = Outside temperature
5. Tp = Temperature at Point P

$$Tp = Ti - ((Ti - To) \times (R2/R1))$$

---

[1] *Moisture Control Hand Book*, Lstiburek and Carmody 1993
[2] Another term for absolute humidity
[3] *Understanding Ventilation*, John Bower 1995
[4] Available from the Trane furnace company
[5] From published R – rating charts
[6] *Controlling Moisture In Homes*, National Association of Home Builders 1987

SECTION NINETEEN

Sample Site Review

BIOGROWTH

CONFIDENTIAL

SITE REVIEW FOR MOLD, MILDEW, FUNGI, AND PATHOGENS

Property Location:

Client:

PURPOSE OF SITE REVIEW:

1. VISUALLY INSPECT FOR AND TO IDENTIFY SUSPECT BIO-GROWTH CONTAMINATED COMPONENTS.
2. DETERMINE CAUSATION
3. SAMPLE [Two Air-o-Cell and two Agar Plates]
4. ASSESS PHYSICAL CONDITION OF CONTAMINATED COMPONENT (S)

☐ Excessive storage and limited visibility. ☐ Odors and Visible Mold @

☐ Cardboard or cellulose materials @

Grade Drainage Concrete Walks Decks	**Roof Gutters Downs Chimney(s)**	Date:
☐ Grade slopes toward house	☐ Over flowing gutters	Start time:
☐ Blocked drains	☐ Damaged downs	End Time:
☐ Ponding water	☐ Defective flashing	
☐ Grade over Parge line	☐ Loose bricks or mortar	Water damage @
☐ High mulch beds	☐ Bio-growth on shingles	
☐ Deck allows water to infiltrate house	☐ Limited roof venting	
	☐ Ice dam damage	
☐ Not Inspected	☐ Not Inspected	
Soffit Fascia Siding Trim	**Basement Crawl Spaces**	
☐ No soffit vents	☐ Odors present at entry	
☐ Blocked soffit vents	☐ High humidity	
☐ Damaged or rotted trim	☐ Efflorescence	
☐ Stains on siding	☐ Water stains ☐ floor ☐ wall ☐ ceiling	
☐ No visible Tyvek	☐ Water damaged components	
☐ Ice dam damage	☐ Moisture per Tramex	
☐ Improper caulk techniques	☐ Standing water	
☐ No visible weep holes in brick veneer	☐ Visible bio-growth	
	☐ Limited ventilation	☐ Samples taken @
		1
☐ Not Inspected	☐ Not Inspected	
Heating Cooling Air Handling	**Interior Walls Trim Floor and Coverings**	
☐ Rusted components	☐ Water stains ☐ floor ☐ wall ☐ ceiling	2.
☐ Humidifier	☐ Water damaged components	
☐ Previous duct cleaning	☐ Moisture per Tramex	
☐ Water stains	☐ Visible bio-growth	
☐ Poor filter hygiene	☐ Ghosting or black stains	3
☐ Improper venting		
		4
☐ Not Inspected	☐ Not Inspected	

Attic Areas:

☐ Water stains   ☐ Active water per Tramex   ☐ Water damaged components   ☐ Limited access

☐ Blocked ventilation   ☐ No ventilation   ☐ Double vapor barrier   ☐ Fan without humidistat

☐ Visible Mold @

Attached Garage:

Executive Summary
Notes & Sketches

[ ]Monitor all moisture stains for activity and repair the cause or source of the stain as required.
[ ] Have unusual odors checked with odor meter or Drager tube analysis.
[ ] Identify and repair source of moisture infiltration at: (See above comments)
[ ] Remove repair or replace water damaged components at: (See above comments)
[ ] Consult a Bio-growth mitigation specialist to remediate conditions listed above
[ ] Consider using a de-humidifier if humidity or moisture exists.
[ ] Review the need to water-proof the basement to stop moisture.
[ ] Ceiling tile panels should be removed immediately if ever wet .
[ ] Install a vapor barrier to minimize moisture over crawl space floor.
[ ] Crawl space a vapor barrier.
[ ] Have the furnace ductwork professionally cleaned.
[ ] Consider adding a high efficiency filter system to the furnace.
[ ] Properly caulk and seal trim around doors and windows.
[ ] Adjust grade or mulch beds to allow water to flow away from the foundation.
[ ] Do not use furnace humidifiers unless necessary due to potential of elevated humidity, which, may transfer to attic areas thereby creating a habitat favorable to mold growth on components.
[ ] This bio-growth site visit is applicable to the date and time of the visit and samples taken only.
[ ] Should have a window, fan or vent installed in the bathroom(s).
[ ] Due to the limited scope of this site visit and minimal sampling, all areas are not reviewed nor are all potentially contaminated areas observed. We suggest an extensive bio-growth investigation.
[ ] Consult our web site for further information on bio-growth, mold, air-borne pathogens, bio-aerosols, information relating to your test results at

www.forensicinspections.com

Table 1. Summary of quantitative standards and guidelines for fungi in air by governmental and private organizations.

Organization/Document/Year	Recommendations	SP[a]	Bases
ACGIH/Guidelines for the Assessment of Bioaerosis[35]/1989	• <100 CFU/m^3 = OK • Indoor/outdoor, 1 = OK if similar taxa • Complaint area/Non-complaint > 10X = usual	Y	Consesus[b]
ACGIH/Air Sampling Instruments for Evaluation of Atmospheric Containment[37]/1995	• <100 CFU/m^3 = low: e.g. cleanrooms and hospitals • 100-1000 CFU/m^3 =intermediate: e.g. general indoor and outdoor concentrations • >1000 CFU/m^3 + high: e.g. animal handling areas	Y	Consesus[b]
AIHA/Biohazards Ref. Manual[36]/1986	• There is no safe level of an uncontained pathogenic organism	N	N/A
AIHA/The industrial Hygienist's Guide to IAQ Investigaitons[40]/1993	• Rank order assesment • Indoor/outdoor comparison recommended	N	Citation[d,35]
AIHA/The practioner's Approach to IAQ Investigations[14]/1989	• Rank order assesment • ≥1000 CFU/m3 = indicates atypical situation • High indoor/outdoor ratio = indoor amplifier present • Cites Miller et al, (1988)[19](See Table 2)	N/A	Citation[19,29,35]

CEC/Report #12: Biological Particles in Indoor Environment[21]/1993	• For houses: >10^{4}CFU/m^3 = very high
	                    >10^{4}CFU/m^3 = high
	                    >10^{4}CFU/m^3 = intermediate
	                    <200 CFU/m^3 = low
	                    (<500 CFU/m^3 on DG18 medium)
	                    <50 CFU/m^3 = very low
	• For non-industrial indoor
	                    >2000 CFU/m^3 = very high
	                    >2000 CFU/m^3 = high
	                    >500 CFU/m^3 = intermediate
	                    >100 CFU/m^3 = low
	                    <25 CFU/m^3 = very low
		Y	Consensus; Survey[22-25]

CMHC/Determination of Fungal Propagules in indoor Air[18]/1988	• 0 CFU/m^3= no action unless indicated by inspection • ≥50 CFU/m^3 if one species = identify source to determine further action • ≤150-200 CFU/m^3 if several species = no action unless indicated by inspection • ≥200 CFU/m^3 if several species = prudence requires further inspection • ≤400-500 CFUm^3 mainly *Cladosporium* and *Alternaria* = no action unless indicated by inspection • ≥5000 CFU/m3 mainly *Cladosporium* and *Alternaria* = determine reason	Y	Citation[18]
CMHC/(Disclaimer)/Testing of older houses for microbiological pollutants[20]/1991	• 0 CFU/m^3= no action unless indicated by inspection and *Cladosporium* = investigate • >500 CFU/m3 including *Alternaria* and *Cladosporium* = investigate • Indoor/outdoor comparison recommended when ≤200 CFU/m^3	Y	Survey; Citation[18]

Cutter Information Corp./IAQ Update: Biocontaminants in Indoor Environments[46]/1994	• Indoor/outdoor ratios range from <0.1 to < 1 =OK
	• Upper limits range from:
	   300 CFU/m^3 of common fungi (e.g. *Cladosporium*)
	   150 CFU/m^3 of mixed species other than pathogenic or toxigenic species
	   200 CFU/m^3 total fungi
	   100 CFU/m^3 unless immunocompromised population
		Y	Citation1[9, 35, 48, 49, 52, 76]

> *There are so many groups offering various threshold levels of microbial contamination, that it is almost impossible to choose a single source to be your baseline. There are no established thresholds - only guidelines.*

Table 2. Summary of quantitative standards and guidelines for fungi in indoor air by investigators.

Investigator	Recommendations	SP[a]	Bases
Berk et al.[50] 1979	• Exposure to 20 CFU/m³ to over 7000 CFU/m³ with no ill effects	N/A[b]	Survey[c]
Burge[55] 1979	• If indoor microbial aerosol's qualitatively different from outdoor and indoor levels consistently more than double outdoor and exceeding 1000 CFU/m³ = investigate	Y	Personal experience[d]
Godish[56] 1991	• >1000 CFU/m³ fungi = high levels; potentially significant contamination • >100 CFU/m³ fungi = Mold-free environment • In between, subject to investigator's own interpretation • Low recovery cannot confirm low airborne mold spore levels	Y	Personal experience
Holmberg[51] 1984	• <2200 CFU/m³ = surface mold present • 10,000 to 15,000 CFU/m³ = surface mold present	N/A	N/A
Lacey et al.[57] 1988	• 10³-10⁴ spores/m3 of total fungi = normal in air	Y	Survey
Miller er al.[19] 1988	• Some fungi not acceptable in indoor air (toxigenic, pathogenic) • ≥50 CFU/m³ one species = investigate • ≤150 CFU/m³ = OK if mixture of species • ≤300 CFU/m³ = OK if common phylloplane fungi	Y	Survey
Miller et al.[52] 1992	• Indoor mycollera qualitativey similar to outdoors = OK • Indoor mycollera quantitatively lower than outdoors = OK	Y	Survey
Morey et al.[52] 1984	• ≥ 1000 CFU/m³ = investigate • ≥ 10⁶ fungi/g dust = investigate • ≥ 105 bacteria or fungi/ml stagnet water or slime = investigate • Levels above do not necessarily imply hazard	Y	Literature review; Personal experience
Ohgke et al.[47] 1987	• >100 CFU/m³ indicates indoor fungal source = further investigation necessary	Y	Survey
Reponen et al.[48] 1990	• >500 CFU/m³ (winter) = abnomal indoor source • Indoor/outdoor > 1 may indicate abnomal indoor levels in summer • Applies only to urban and suburban subarctic homes	Y	Survey
Reynolds et al.[53] 1990	• >500 CFU/m³ = abnomal condition • Significant indoor/outdoor differences indicate indoor sources • Speciation and rank ordering recommended	Y	Survey
Solomon et al.[54] 1984	• Domestic interior levels range from 1-6000/m3 • Maximum levels usually <1600/m³	N	Survey
Yang et al.[49] 1993	• 200 CFU/m3 total fungi upper limit • Critical analysis if opportunistic or toxigenic fungi detected	Y	Survey

[a]Sampling protocol; [b]Not available; [c]Based on data from a survey; [d]Based on field experiences of investigator

Volume 46 September 1996

[1] Journal of Air and Waste Management Association Volume 46 1996

SECTION TWENTY ONE

Definitions and Related Information

DEFINITIONS

- **Abatement** – Suppression, termination, or removal.
- **Acceptable Indoor Air Temperatures** – (Summer 74.0°F – 80.0°F; Winter 68.5°F- 76.5°F; Both are for Dry bulb at 30% relative humidity) (Summer 73.0°F – 79.0°F; Winter 68.5°F – 74.5°F for Dry bulb at 50% relative humidity)
- **Acceptable Indoor Air Humidity** – (30-60%)
- **AFD** – Air Filtration Device
- **Aerosol** – A vapor or mist
- **Aerosolizes** – Made into a vapor or mist
- **AIAQC** – American Indoor Air Quality Council
- **AIHA** – American Industrial Hygiene Association
- **Airlock** – A system for permitting ingress or egress without permitting air movement between a contaminated area and an un-contaminated area. Typically, an airlock is seen in three curtained doorways at least 3 feet a part in decontamination units.
- **Air Monitoring** – The process of measuring the mold spores of a specific volume of air in a time interval.
- **AHU** – Air Handling Unit providing ventilation, heating, and cooling.
- **Air exchanges** - Ventilation systems are designed and installed in buildings to replace stale, contaminated air with fresh air from the outside. Air enters and leaves a house in several other ways too. It can enter by infiltration, through construction joints and cracks around windows and doors, through the foundation, and crawl spaces. Air also enters through natural ventilation openings, such as open doors and windows. The rate at which outdoor air replaces indoor air is the "exchange rate." It measures how many times the complete volume of air inside the house is replaced with fresh outside air. In typical U.S. homes, the average exchange rate is 0.7 to 1.0 complete air exchanges per hour. In tight homes, the exchange rate can be as low as 0.02 complete air exchanges per hour. In leaky homes, it may be as high as 2.0 complete air changes per hour.
- **Allergenic molds** - Normally not dangerous, but they can cause allergic or asthmatic symptoms; such as, wheezing or runny nose. These molds can be abated safely without the assistance of a professional. It is suggested that personal protection, in the form of gloves and disposable particulate-removing respirator be used, especially in those who experience allergies and/or asthma.
- **Ambient Air Temperature** – The air temperature on the exterior.
- **Amplification or Amplify** – Make large, increase and in fungal term, means fungi grows.
- **Anderson Plate Testing** – Method of testing viable mold spores. The unit is a culture plated for impacted sampling.
- **ANSI** – American National Standards Institute
- **APF** – Assigned Protection Factor
- **Aw** (water activity) the amount of water available to the surface usually .55 to 1.0.
- **Bias Tests** – False positive or false negative can occur due to weather condition and season of the year.
- **Bioaerosols** – Are generally airborne particles that either are living things or come from living things. Living things for this definition are described as kingdoms. There are five kingdoms: fungi, mineral, protoctista, plantae and animalia.
- **Biocide** - Substance or chemical that kills organisms, such as molds.
- **Bio-growth** - Any substance that looks like mold/ mildew / moss / fungus / growth or similar. You cannot determine the difference between mold / mildew / moss / or some type of environmental growth from a visual inspection. Laboratory analysis is needed to properly define the substance in question.
- **Bleach Solution** - A mixture or morality of 15 parts water to 1 part chlorine bleach.
- **Bio-pollution means** – The same as Bio-growth and all other living pollution types.
- **CIH** – Certified Industrial Hygienist
- **CIE** – Certified Indoor Environmentalist
- **CMR** – Certified Mold Remediator
- **Contaminant** – Any physical, chemical, biological, or radioactive substance can have an adverse effect on air, water, soil, or any other interior of exterior surface. CONTAMINANT defined by the "Institute from Inspection, Cleaning and Restoration Certification (IICRC) S-500" – any physical, chemical, biological or radioactive substance that can have an adverse effect on air, water or soil, or any other interior or exterior surface.
- **Containment** – The act or condition of containing. Contain – to keep under proper control. CONTAINMENT defined by *Webster's College Dictionary* – the act or condition of containing. Contain to keep under proper control.
- **Competent Person** – a person trained in all aspects of mold

testing, mitigation, interpretation of results, and application of the scope of work to a specific site situation.

- **Clean Room** – A clean room is one that is not contaminated. Typically, the clean room is the last room in a decontamination three-room system.
- **Containment Barrier** – Polyethylene sheeting that seals off the work areas to prevent cross contamination and to prevent distribution of contamination to surrounding clean areas.
- **Critical Barrier** – Layers of six-mil polyethylene sheeting that seal off the physical penetrations of the site work area; i.e. soffit, fan vents, roof venting windows, registers, duct work, and like openings or breeches, etc.
- **Decontamination Enclosure System** – A series of connected rooms, with curtained doorways between any two adjacent rooms, for the decontamination of workers or materials and equipment. A decontamination enclosure system always contains at least two airlocks. The decontamination system will have a clean room, shower room, and equipment room with airlocks between each room and will be connected to the work area or contamination area.
- **De-water** – Remove water from an uncontrolled event, such as a flood. De-water equipment could be a dehumidifier.
- **Dew point temperature** - Dew point temperature is the temperature below which moisture will condense out of air. Air that is holding as much water vapor as possible is saturated or at its dew point. Water will condense on a surface, such as a building wall, attic sheathing, basement foundation, or pitcher of ice water that is at or below the dew point temperature of the air.
- **Dry-Bulb Temperature** - Dry bulb temperature is the air temperature determined by an ordinary thermometer. The dry bulb temperature scale is located at the base of the chart. Vertical lines indicate constant dry bulb temperature. The TV weatherman uses this unit for temperature.
- **EIFS** – Exterior insulation facade system or fascia system. EX: Stucco, Drivit or Exterior cladding.
- **EPA** – Environmental Protection Agency
- **Equipment Room** – A contaminated room that is generally part of a decontamination enclosure system.
- **ERV** – Energy Recovery Ventilator
- **Event** – A moisture related occurrence, happening, effect, or result that has the potential to initiate or affect fungal activity.
- **Full Face Respirator** – A respirator that covers the entire face of the person wearing it.
- **Fit tests** – Process to test respirators on individuals. All respirators that are to be worn should be fit tested prior to use. Only certified personnel can perform fit testing.
- **FUNGI** - Any of numerous plants of the Fifth Kingdom, ranging in form from a single cell to a body mass of branched filamentous hyphae.
- **Gray water** – Dirty water that contains contaminants.
- **Hoarfrost** - Are moisture conditions that occur in the attics of dwellings. Related to moisture that forms when the temperature and relative humidity are in a specific ratio.

This moisture can be the source of the water needed for spore activity to amplify in the attic. Dew point is moisture in the summer and hoarfrost is the water crystals that form in the winter.

- **HEPA Filter** – A high efficiency particulate absolute filter capable of trapping and retaining 99.97 percent of particulate matter greater than 0.3 microns in diameter.
- **HEPA Vacuum** – A vacuum cleaner that contains a HEPA filter.
- **HRV** – Heat Recovery Ventilator
- **Hyphae** - Refer to single, unidentifiable fragments of mold. Although they may not be traceable to a specific mold species, the fragments themselves may be responsible for allergic reactions in some people and may indicate a previous or current growth event in humans and animals. Health effects range from short-term irritation to immunosuppression to cancer and even death. If any toxic molds are identified, it is suggested that you seek advice from an Industrial Hygienist or other mold professional. The average homeowner should NOT attempt the abatement of these types of mold.
- **Industrial Hygienist** – IH is a qualified person that performs duties with environmental health hazards.
- **IAQ** – Indoor Air Quality
- **IAQA** – Indoor Air Quality Association
- **Interim Control** – Time between, meantime or temporary method for a condition that would otherwise require repair, remediation, or abatement.
- **Interstitial** - Space moisture contamination is when, under the right conditions of temperature and humidity, moisture is created in the wall cavity or behind vinyl wallpaper.
- **Isolation Barrier** – Two layers of 6-mil polyethylene sheeting that seals off the site work area.
- **Label** – Instructions that come will all chemical products. The MSDS are part of the label or vise versa.
- **Microbe** – A microbe is a group of very small life forms. Microbes are so small that they usually can only be seen while using a microscope. They are also bio-aerosols and are grouped as viruses, bacteria, and fungi.
- **Micron** – One millionth of a meter, also know as a micrometer. This is approximately 1/25,000th of an inch. To give you a sense of scale, the average human hair is approximately 75 microns in diameter.
- **Mildew** - A superficial covering or discoloring of organic materials caused by fungi, esp. under damp conditions. Commonly called white mildew.
- **Mold or Mould** - Any of various fungus growths often causing disintegration of organic matter
- **Mold Measurements** - Mold is measured in counts per cubic meter (Cm^3) - the number of spores in a one-meter cube of air. A mold count of 0-500 counts per cubic meter of air Cm^3 is considered low, 500-1500 counts Cm^3 is moderate, and a count of 1501 and greater qualifies as high. Mold problems are more common in summer and gradually decline from September through November.
- **MVOC's** – Microbial volatile organic compounds.

- **MSDS** – Material Safety Data Sheet
- **Mycotoxins** – A toxin metabolite produced by fungi.
- **NEC** – National Electrical Code.
- **Negative Pressure** – An atmosphere created in the site work area enclosure such that dust, mold spores, or other airborne contaminates are sucked or drawn through a filtration system.
- **NIOSH** – National Institute for Occupational Safety and Health, which was established by the Occupational Safety and Health Act of 1970.
- **OSHA** – Occupational Safety and Health Administration. This was created by the Occupational Safety and Health ACT of 1970.
- **Pathogenic** - MOLD can cause serious health effects in people with suppressed immune systems, those taking chemotherapy, those with HIV/AIDS, or auto-immunity disorders. If any pathogenic molds are identified in this report, it is suggested you seek the advice of an Industrial Hygienist or other mold professional for guidance. The average homeowner should NOT attempt the abatement of these types of mold.
- **Pesticides** - Products such as insecticides, herbicides, rodenticide, and fungicides are all considered "pesticides". A pesticide is defined as any product intended for preventing, destroying, repelling, or mitigating any pest or a plant growth regulator, defoliant, or desicant
- **PAT** – Post abatement test.
- **PEL** – Permissible Exposure Limit as stated by OSHA rules.
- **Photomicrographs** – Pictures taken through a microscope.
- **PHS** – Potentially contaminated homes.
- **Polyethylene Barrier** – For this book, this is 6 mil plastic membrane or sheathing.
- **PPE** – Personnel protection equipment.
- **Pressurization or positive pressure** – This means that air is being blown into a room rather than being sucked out. Example would be a heating vent that is blowing into a room with the door shut and no cold air return. This room is pressurized or under positive pressure.
- **Psychrometric Chart** - A chart used for determining moisture, humidity, dew points, and other indoor air quality conditions. Mostly used as a tool in the drying industry.
- **PVC** – Generally known as plastic plumbing pipes or polyvinyl chloride, earth or clay, greasy, viscous mud, mire, viscous secretion.
- **Relative Humidity** - Relative humidity is a measure of how much moisture is present compared to how much moisture the air could hold at that temperature. Relative humidity is expressed as a percent.
- **Remediation** - defined by *Webster's College Dictionary* – fix; EPA's "Mold Remediation in Schools and Commercial Buildings" - correction of something defective or deficient.
- **Reservoir** – Large supply or area for storage. In fungi terms means a mass of fungi or many colonies of fungi.
- **Sick Building Syndrome** - 0.94, optimum Aw (water activity) ->0.98. Several strains of this fungus (S. atra, S. chartarum and S. alternans are synonymous) may produce a trichothecene mycotoxin- Satratoxin H - which is poisonous by inhalation.

The toxins are present on the fungal spores. This is a slow growing fungus on media. It does not compete well with other rapidly growing fungi. The dark colored fungi grows on building material with high cellulose content and low nitrogen content. Areas with relative humidity above 55 percent and subject to temperature fluctuations are ideal for toxin production. Individuals with chronic exposure to the toxin produced by this fungus reported cold and flu symptoms, sore throats, diarrhea, headaches, fatigue, dermatitis, intermittent local hair loss, and generalized malaise. The toxins produced by this fungus will suppress the immune system affecting the lymphoid tissue and the bone marrow. Animals injected with the toxin from this fungus exhibited the following symptoms: necrosis and hemorrhage within the brain, thymus, spleen, intestine, lung, heart, lymph node, liver, and kidney. The mycotoxin is also reported to be a liver and kidney carcinogen. Affects by absorption of the toxin in the human lung are known as pneumomycosis. This organism is rarely found in outdoor samples. It is usually difficult to find in indoor air samples unless it is physically disturbed. The spores are in a gelatinous mass. Appropriate media for the growth of this organism will have high cellulose content and low nitrogen content. The spores will die readily after release. The dead spores are still allergenic and toxigenic. Percutaneous absorption has caused mild symptoms.

- **Surface Wipe Sampling or Swab Sampling** – A method of testing surfaces using a sterile swab to determine microbial contamination
- **TLV** – Threshold Limit Values are established by the American Conference of Governmental Industrial Hygienists. Workers can be exposed with minimal or no adverse health effects to these levels.
- **Vapor diffusion** - The ability of water or moisture to travel to areas of lesser moisture activity.
- **Vapor pressure** – air contains varying amounts of moisture in the gas or vapor form.
- **VBS / VHS** – Vacant building syndrome or vacant home syndrome. This is when an uncontrolled event occurs in a vacant building or home. This is due to moisture and humidity and a non-conditioned building or home. Fungal reservoirs amplify throughout and contaminated the entire building and home.
- **VOC's** – Volatile organic compounds. Compounds that vaporize rapidly.
- **Wet-Bulb Temperature** - Wet bulb temperature reflects the cooling effect of evaporating water (like drying your hands in one of those public bathroom wall push button air dryers). Wet bulb temperature can be determined by passing air over a thermometer that has been wrapped with a small amount of moist fabric. The cooling effect of the evaporating water causes a lower temperature compared to the dry bulb ambient air temperature.
- **Water activity** - The amount of water available to the surface of a wall, etc. (Aw)

SECTION TWENTY TWO

Bibliography and Acknowledgements

BIBLIOGRAPHY

- ASHRAE American Society of Heating Refrigeration and Air Conditioning Engineers Inc.

- *Bioaerosols Assessment and Control*, <u>Macher et al</u>, ACGIH, ISBN 882417-29-1

- *Controlling Moisture in Homes*, National Association of Home Builders, 1987 ISBN 0-86718-302-0

- *IAQ and Efflorescence*, Ever wonder what the white stuff is? Paul Cocrane

- Indoor allergens Institute of Medicine Nation Academy Press

- *Microfungi*, <u>Gravesen et al</u>, 2001 ISBN 87-16-11436-1

- Miller, Aerotech Monitor, Volume 4 Issuer 3

- *Moisture Control Handbook*, <u>Lstiburek / Carmody</u> 1993 ISBN 0-442-01432-5

- Moisture Control Handbook, Lstiburek J., Camrmody., Building, Science Corp., Chestnut Hill, Massachusetts, Underground Space Center University of Minnesota, ITP 1993, Van Nostrand Reinhold

- *Mycology of Air workshop on airborne fungal particulates.* Sponsored by the Pan American Aerobiology Association, May 1999, Tucson, Arizona. John Haines Beatriz Escamilla-Garcia, Michael Muilenberg, Janet Gallup, Estelle Levetin, faculty. P. D. Milner, S.A. Olenchock, E. Epstein, R. Rylander, MD, J.Haines, J. Walker, B.L. Ooi, &M. Mariatato, 1995. Bioaerosols associated with composting facilities, Compost Utilization 2: 6-57.

- *Mycology of Air*, A workshop manual for sampling and identifying fungal spores, John Haines

- *Restorative Drying*, <u>Blackburn</u>, DRI-EAZ Products Inc 1999

- *Standard and Reference Guide for Professional Water Damage Restoration*, IICRC S500 Institute of Inspection, Cleaning and Restoration Certification

- *Survey of Quantitative Standards for Fungi in air be government and Private organizations* Charts 1 & 2, Journal of Air and Waste management Association Volume 46 1996

- *The Healthy House: How to Buy One, How to Build One, How to Cure a Sick One*, Bower, J., Lyle Stuart Inc, Secaucus, NJ. 1989

- *Understanding Ventilation*, <u>John Bower</u>, 1995, ISBN 0-9637156-5-8

- www.slcc.edu/tech/techsp/asch/courses/ARCH1210/Lecture/Vapotbar/aiarflow.htm

- Harriet M. Ammann, Ph.D., D.A.B.T. Senior Toxicologist Washington State Department of Health Olympia, Washington

ACKNOWLEDGEMENTS

- 100,000 Images by Marko and Myron Images for anything 216.431.TEST or 216.581.RAD1

- Aero Tech Laboratories

- American Lung Association

- Anderson Instruments of Smyrna Georgia 1.800.736.6898

- California Dept of Health Services

- Connie Jenkins of Environmental Testing and Technology

- Dr. John Shane McCrones Research Institute Inc. of Chicago

- EMSL Laboratories *www.emsl.com*

- Enviro Team Inc.

- Forensic Imaging Inc. and Ambassador Construction Consultants Inc.

- Hands Down Software, Psychrometric Analysis, *www.handsdownsoftware.com*

- John Haines Mycology of Air

- Kansas State University Extension Services

- Minnesota Department of Health Indoor Air Program

- New York City Dept of Health

- Ohio State University Mycology web site Dust Mites

- Pro Lab

- Professional Equipment Co. 1.800.334.9291 or on the web at *www.professionalequipment.com*

- Public domain web sites

- Spruce Environmental Technologies

- Wall Check™

- Zefon Corporation

SECTION TWENTY THREE
About The Authors

Myron S. Ryglewicz CIE, CMR has been a residential environmental property assessor since 1992. He has developed interactive mold investigation site protocols, published nationally mold and lead reports in addition to a general report for home inspectors. He is an active member of the IAQA, AIAQC and ASHI.

With the media, he has been a resource of information for radon, water infiltration, mold reporting, and commentary. He has in process a patent application for the *Forensic Surface Sampling System*, and has implemented strategic mold investigative reporting systems. Myron is considered by the legal community as an expert in mold investigations.

Myron's company, Forensic Imaging Inc., maintains a consumer oriented web site at **www.forensicinspections.com**. His company conducts initial and clearance tests for mold mitigation, and analyzes for the identification of fungi and pollen spores.

Myron is a continuing education instructor and has spoken nationally on the topic of "Mold in the Home." In his continual quest for education he has attended Concordia University Bachelor of Arts in Education; Kent State University; McCrones Research Institute–Microscopy; Georgia Institute of Technology-Environmental Property Assessment; University of Cincinnati-Lead Inspector and Risk Assessor Training; University of Findlay-Lead Risk Assessor continuing education and Rutgers University-Initial Radon Certification. Myron has completed thousands of property inspections and environmental investigations.

Marko Emil Vovk has more than 25 years of experience as a professional in building inspection, construction materials laboratory testing, environmental consulting and expert witness testimony.

As a civil engineer, inspector and environmentalist, he has inspected over 6800 commercial and residential buildings. Projects include many high-rise buildings, gaming facilities, medical buildings, industrial sites, schools and residential homes. He holds current state licenses in radon gas, lead paint, and wood-boring insects, including fungicides and pesticides. Certifications also include, 203K, Certified Indoor Air Environmentalist (CIE), and HVAC air balancer.

Marko, and his company Ambassador Construction Consultants Inc., is considered by consumer radio and television to be an expert in construction issues.

Mr. Vovk was the contributing author to three nationally distributed reporting systems that include lead, mold, and home inspection disciplines.

Mr. Vovk holds one US patent and has developed integrative mold investigation site protocols. He is an active member of Indoor Air Quality Association, American Indoor Air Quality Council, American Society of Home Inspectors, and many other professional organizations. He can be reached at Clevelandmold@aol.com.

www.reainc.com
www.forensicinspections.com

SECTION TWENTY FOUR

Index

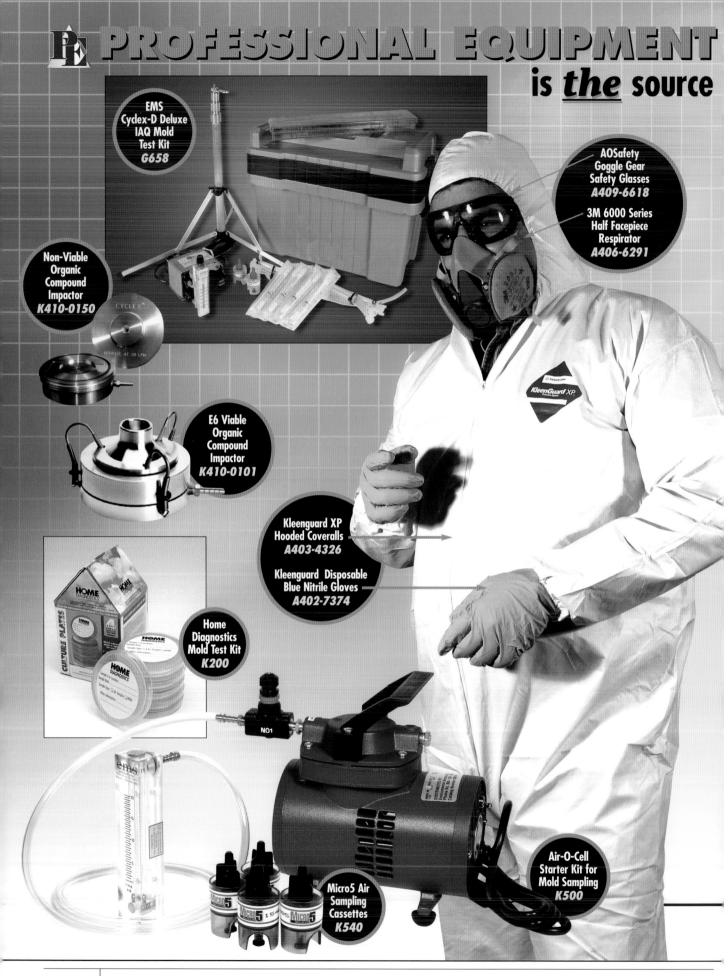

PROFESSIONAL EQUIPMENT

is *the* source

EMS Cyclex-D Deluxe IAQ Mold Test Kit
G658

AOSafety Goggle Gear Safety Glasses
A409-6618

3M 6000 Series Half Facepiece Respirator
A406-6291

Non-Viable Organic Compound Impactor
K410-0150

E6 Viable Organic Compound Impactor
K410-0101

Kleenguard XP Hooded Coveralls
A403-4326

Kleenguard Disposable Blue Nitrile Gloves
A402-7374

Home Diagnostics Mold Test Kit
K200

Micro5 Air Sampling Cassettes
K540

Air-O-Cell Starter Kit for Mold Sampling
K500

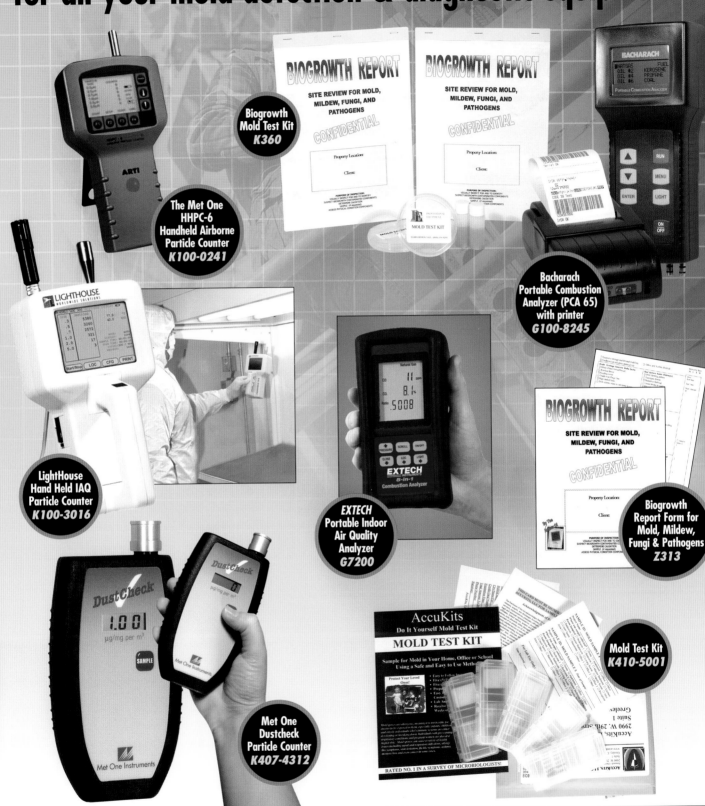

for all your mold detection & diagnostic equipment!

Biogrowth Mold Test Kit K360

The Met One HHPC-6 Handheld Airborne Particle Counter K100-0241

Bacharach Portable Combustion Analyzer (PCA 65) with printer G100-8245

LightHouse Hand Held IAQ Particle Counter K100-3016

EXTECH Portable Indoor Air Quality Analyzer G7200

Biogrowth Report Form for Mold, Mildew, Fungi & Pathogens Z313

Met One Dustcheck Particle Counter K407-4312

Mold Test Kit K410-5001

www.professionalequipment.com 800.334.9291

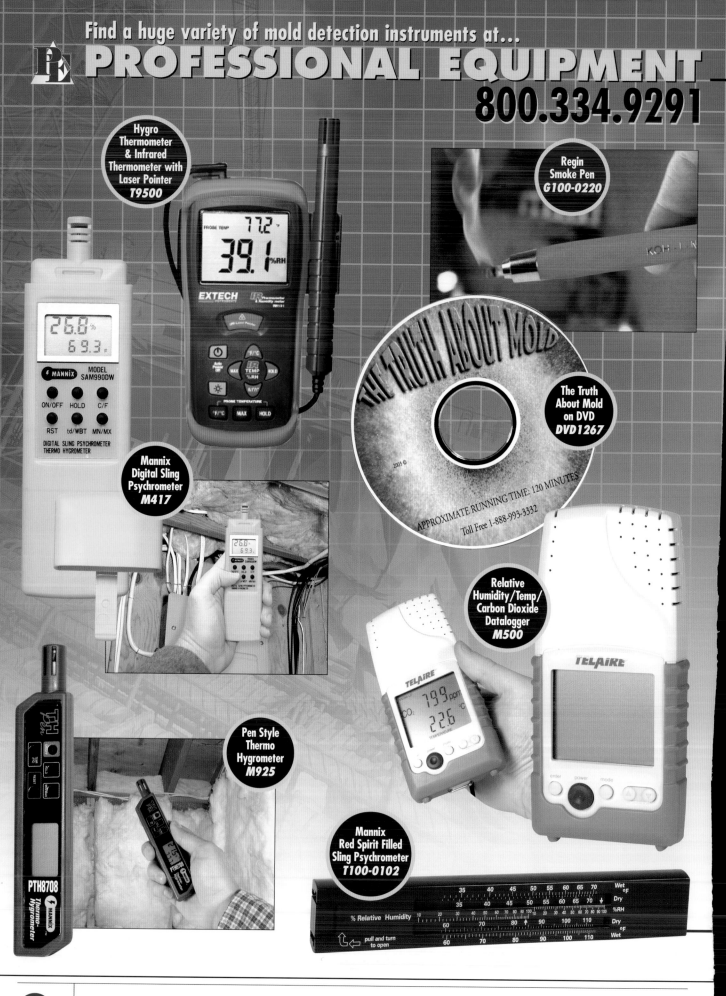

Find a huge variety of mold detection instruments at...

PROFESSIONAL EQUIPMENT

800.334.9291

Hygro Thermometer & Infrared Thermometer with Laser Pointer
T9500

Regin Smoke Pen
G100-0220

The Truth About Mold on DVD
DVD1267

Mannix Digital Sling Psychrometer
M417

Relative Humidity/Temp/ Carbon Dioxide Datalogger
M500

Pen Style Thermo Hygrometer
M925

Mannix Red Spirit Filled Sling Psychrometer
T100-0102

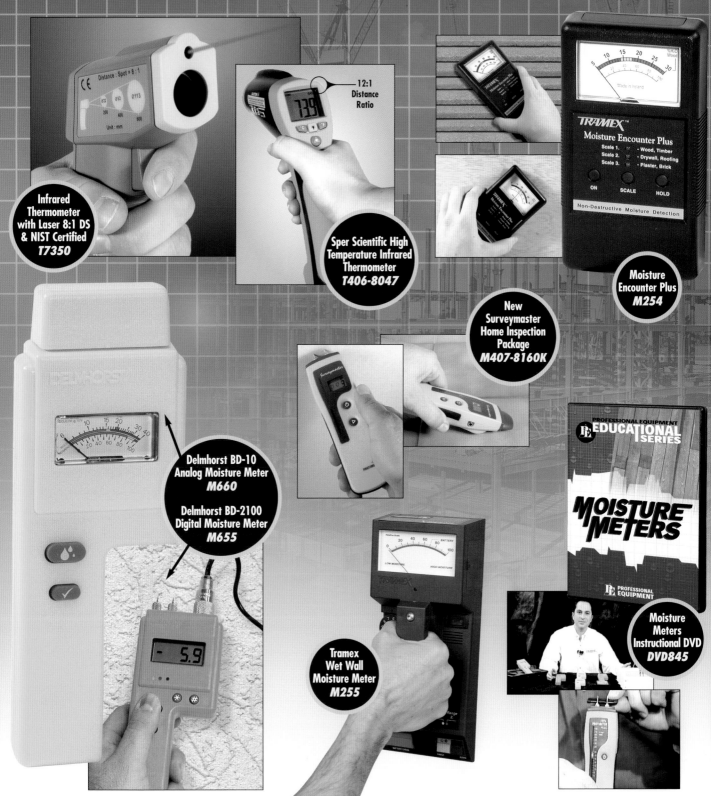

We can help solve your mold problems!

Infrared Thermometer with Laser 8:1 DS & NIST Certified T7350

12:1 Distance Ratio

Sper Scientific High Temperature Infrared Thermometer T406-8047

TRAMEX™ Moisture Encounter Plus
- Scale 1. - Wood, Timber
- Scale 2. - Drywall, Roofing
- Scale 3. - Plaster, Brick

ON   SCALE   HOLD

Non-Destructive Moisture Detection

Moisture Encounter Plus M254

New Surveymaster Home Inspection Package M407-8160K

Delmhorst BD-10 Analog Moisture Meter M660

Delmhorst BD-2100 Digital Moisture Meter M655

PROFESSIONAL EQUIPMENT EDUCATIONAL SERIES

MOISTURE METERS

PROFESSIONAL EQUIPMENT

Moisture Meters Instructional DVD DVD845

Tramex Wet Wall Moisture Meter M255

www.professionalequipment.com   800.334.9291

NOTES

NOTES

NOTES